Through My Mother's Eyes

TOM SERINO

Contents

To my parents.

While it is difficult to encapsulate seventy years of life and love into so few pages, I dedicate this book to you both, honored to share your story with the world. You have left an indelible mark on the lives of all who have known you—family, friends, and neighbors—and this is your true legacy, a gift of love and service that has enriched the lives of countless people.

May all who read this narrative see the transforming and life-giving power of unconditional love and acceptance.

"Parents are the pride of their children."
Proverbs 17:6 NIV

Tommy & Doris, 1950

Prologue

The rhythmic sound of tires on the damp macadam produced a comforting symphony as I drive through New Jersey, amid cars jockeying for position at moderate speeds, on the way to Mamma's house. Just three weeks has passed since Pop's funeral, and the familiar highway and its typical commuters give a melancholy reminder of the events of the last twenty days.

The phone call informing us of Pop's fall had lacked urgency, and since we'd planned to leave the next day for a weekend visit, we didn't alter our prearranged travel details. Pop was in the hospital and had been diagnosed with pneumonia, but his condition gave no indication of peril. Then, as we approached the exit for the New York State Thruway, we received a phone call. Pop had passed.

Numbness and profound sorrow washed over me in waves. Pop was gone, and the void he left was far greater than anyone could ever have imagined. Though the all-consuming sadness overwhelmed me, I suddenly imagined my mother. How was she? How would she handle this?

After spending seventy-three years with Pop, suddenly—without warning, without mercy—he was forever removed from her embrace in one callous twist of fate's cruel plan.

Seven days later at his funeral, I watched as she entered the room where he lay. She was dutifully adorned in traditional black, and her beautiful face was pinched with sorrow too deep for verbal expression. She approached him without hesitation and spoke to him softly, touching him gently and frequently as if to store the sensory stimulation that would help her endure the rest of her life. The multitude of sweet words and caresses intended to transcend death and carry her love directly to his waiting soul. Brokenness and grief blended perfectly with strength and resiliency as she embodied the precise characteristics of the blessed mother of sorrows.

Now, I wonder how I'll find her faring. After three weeks of emptiness, the merciful numbness of shock will have worn off and her bleeding broken heart will be exposed to the cruel reality of his absence.

I pull into the driveway and take a moment to gather my thoughts—to enclose my emotions within the chambers of my soul to be addressed at a more opportune moment, and to collect all the fragments of perseverance necessary to assist my mother along this lonely journey to wholeness.

Opening the door of the house they'd shared for decades, I call out, "Mamma! It's me." Inside, I remove my shoes and place them evenly against the wall, then straighten.

Mamma comes from the kitchen with a bright smile on her face. "Hi, baby. How was your trip?"

After sixty-five years on this earth, to be referred to as "baby" by my mother is in no way insulting or demeaning. Rather, it's endearing that, although I sport white hair and have children and grandchildren of my own, my mother looks at me with a maternal love and concern that is unending. "It was fine. Long and arduous, to be honest." Finding no need to share with her the sadness that accompanied this journey, I embrace her and kiss her, feeling the frailness of a body having experienced eighty-eight years of life's trials and triumphs.

We walk into the living room, and she goes to the large chair and its small side table, on which sits a steaming cup of aromatic tea. She expends tremendous effort in descending to the level of the chair and grins with obvious relief once the task is completed.

My mother had always been a handsome woman, with soft skin, a light complexion, and piercing green eyes. Her thick, wavy dark hair fell to her shoulders and accented her delicate facial features as a frame encircles a priceless portrait. Much has changed with the passing of the long, difficult years, though. Age, infirmity, and now grief have taken their toll on her once young and robust body. Her snow-white hair is cut short to prevent further thinning. Her eyes are obscured behind thick glasses due to her weakening vision. Even when she's in a seated position, the awkward twisting and bending of her torso reveals little support from her spine or hips. The most common movements involve concentrated effort, and the simplest activities are subject to deep consideration because of the energy required.

Yet despite the inevitable decline that comes with age, Mamma has qualities deep within the recesses of her being that give her the strength and resilience to persevere through any of life's storms. She has endured infirmity, adversity, disappointment, and fear, and through it grown strong, with a will that is undeterred. The irony of her present state is that although her physical body is weakening, diminishing her basic skills and making every painstaking action difficult, her inner spirit defies the natural decline and grows stronger, with greater resolve at every turn.

She reaches for her tea and slowly draws it to her lips, and one sip seems to revive her fatigue.

"How have you been these last few weeks, Ma? Are you sleeping well? Have you been eating regularly?" I try not to sound overly concerned, but the anxiety is evident in my voice, even to me.

"Oh, you guys shouldn't worry so much," she responds. "I'm doing fine. Someone has been here every day since Dad passed. But you know, I am able to stay by myself. I don't need a babysitter. After all, I raised all of you." She's definitely feeling better. I sense in her protests that she longs for things to be as they were before and isn't quite ready to accept her new situation in life.

Then she backs down from her frustration and shares the details of the past three weeks. "Your sister has been a blessing. She took me to the bank to remove Dad's name from the accounts and replace it with her name. This was what Dad wanted. We'd discussed all of these things months ago. I think he had a sense that he wasn't going to be around much longer, and he wanted to make sure that I was taken care of. That was your father. He was always worried about me. He always watched over me."

Her voice trails off and she pauses for a moment, then takes another sip of tea. "Your father was a good man, the best. He never thought of himself. He always put me first. Oh, he was hardheaded and stubborn, and we argued and fought more often than not. But I knew that he loved me. I knew that he was ready to give his life for me. And he did. He lived his life for me."

A sigh escapes from deep within her chest. "It's hard to believe that he's gone. I keep waiting to hear him call my name. Sometimes I really do think I hear his voice. He's in everything I see. He's in every thought I think, and I feel so lost. What do I do now? How do I start over again without him after seventy-three years together? I don't think that's possible. I don't really want to try."

To steer the conversation back to a more positive perspective, I focus on their life together rather than his all-too-recent absence. "I know that you guys were together for a long time. When did you first meet Dad?"

This is a question I've never asked before, and why at this moment the thought entered my mind, I don't know. But now that the question has been posed, I'm genuinely curious about the events that brought my parents together for what would be a lifetime.

Mamma turns toward the table beside her and retrieves a small, framed black-and-white photo of the two of them from behind the teacup. I've seen it countless times before —the one where they appear to be in their late teens, and both are smiling brightly as Dad has his arm around Mamma. A tree devoid of leaves stands to their left, and just beyond them is the Hudson River.

Mamma holds the photo in both hands, sits back in the chair, and stares at it for a few moments. Then resting her head back, she fixes her gaze on the ceiling and smiles as if remembering.

ONE

First Meeting

I was fifteen years old the first time I saw your father. It was 1948, after the war years, and we lived in Poughkeepsie on South Clover Street near Delano Street. Those houses are all gone now—urban renewal secured their demise—but back then it was a nice residential neighborhood. I was coming home from the library, and I decided to stop at a friend's house. Ida Cosa was my best friend from Christopher Columbus School. We had graduated from the eighth grade together, but since we began high school, I hadn't spent much time with her.

Ida lived on the corner of Union and Perry Streets, right near the candy store. As I climbed the steps to the front porch, she must have heard my footsteps. It was a warm spring day, and the windows were open to refresh the house of its winter staleness. She came out on the porch and greeted me warmly. With Ida, each time we met it was as if a long-neglected relationship was suddenly restored.

While we were on her front porch talking, I noticed a group of boys congregated on the corner, directly in front of the candy store. They were growing brassier yet remaining affable in their interactions, and I wondered whether their demonstrations were for the benefit of Ida and me. As they continued their comical exchanges, one young man was slightly more conspicuous. He was a rakish lad with an enchanting countenance and an impish grin. His curly black hair dropped provocatively onto his forehead, and although it was yet springtime, his face was already tanned. A gregarious fellow, he seemed to require much attention from the group and projected a slightly disreputable quality that bordered on arrogance.

I couldn't look away from him, but when he glanced in my direction and smiled, I flushed and turned away quickly, embarrassed to have been caught staring. Then moments later, he was there on the sidewalk in front of Ida's house. I faced him, with Ida securely by my side.

Ignoring Ida he looked directly into my eyes and spoke. "Hi. How are you?"

An uncomfortable pause ensued.

"Doris, do you know Tommy Serino?" Ida asked me as I stood frozen in place, unsure of how to respond.

"Uh, no," I finally said. "I'm happy to meet you."

"You're Kay Messina's sister, right? That's what some of the boys were saying."

Everyone knew Kay. She was two years older than me and strikingly beautiful with red hair and a milk-white complexion. Kay was popular with the boys and never lacked male company. I always felt like the ugly duckling in her shadow.

"Some of us are going up to Canon Street this Friday night, to the dance. Maybe I'll see you there." And without waiting for a response, he left to rejoin his friends.

I wasn't sure what to think of this awkward exchange.

He didn't seem like the kind of young man with whom I would want to associate. He was brazen and audacious, actually quite arrogant in my estimation. A wise guy—that's the term that seemed to describe him best. I was certain that I didn't like him and we would never be friends.

After saying goodbye to Ida, I descended the steps and continued on my way home. The group of boys proceeded down Perry Street, and Tommy looked back over his shoulder and grinned.

My face immediately reddened, and I averted my gaze and quickened my pace down Union Street.

"There you are," my mother called out as I entered the house. "Hurry up and set the table. Dinner is almost ready."

"Okay, Mom. I'll be right there." I rushed to put my library books in the bedroom I shared with my sister and passed my father taking a well-deserved nap on the sofa. Daddy ran an industrial sewing machine at Goldcrest Fashions, the pocketbook factory uptown. It was a long day of standing behind the huge, noisy devise and repeating the same monotonous stitches endlessly.

During the summertime, he endured the claustrophobic atmosphere of the stifling, humid factory as the combination of the heat and the pedestal fans converted the working floor into a convection oven. The scorched air was filled with the aroma of leather, machine oil, and perspiration as clouds of dust floated to the ceiling's highest points and back to the floor again. In the winter, winds found every flaw in the factory walls and the broken windows which should have been replaced in the summer now permitted frigid arctic cold to permeate the factory numbing hands and feet and making leather purses hard and unyielding and difficult to manipulate. But this was springtime. The weather was warm, the breezes were refreshing, and life in the factory was at its best.

In the kitchen, my mother and sister were already putting dinner on the table. Kay had set the table for me, and I gave her a thankful look that she intuitively understood. Sororal communication often requires no words.

"Joe! Come on, dinner's ready!" my mother called. "Doris, go get your father,"

Mom ordered impatiently. I went into the living room and bent over and kissed my sleeping dad on his forehead. "Time for dinner, Daddy," I whispered.

He opened his eyes and smiled. His gaze was always filled with affection for his girls. Dad was an easygoing man, while Mom was the disciplinarian in the family. She was a good and loving mother but very limited in her displays of affection. She was strict and managed her home in an orderly fashion.

We always knew what day it was by what household chores were accomplished: Monday was wash day, Tuesday was the day for ironing, and so it continued throughout the week only to be repeated in precisely the same order the following week. Saturday was the day to clean the entire house. Bed linens were changed, rugs were beaten, and the entire house was dusted. All chores had to be completed thoroughly before we could go out.

"Joe," Mom said as Dad sat down at the table, "you have to empty the tray underneath the ice box after dinner. I'm afraid it's going to overflow all over the kitchen, and I just washed the floors today." (It must have been Wednesday.)

We didn't have a refrigerator at that time. Our food was kept cold in a large wooden ice box with stainless-steel latches. The iceman would come around the neighborhood every day, and any household needing ice would put a square card in the window. Each corner of the card posted a different price: 10 cents, 15 cents, 25 cents, or 50 cents, indicating the size of the block of ice that was needed.

The iceman would check the card and cut the ice accordingly. Then using large tongs, he would carry the block of ice on his back up the stairs and into the kitchen. After lifting the top of the ice box, putting in the block of ice, and chopping it to ensure that it fit properly, he would replace the lid, collect his coins, and be on his way to the next house in need of his services.

Underneath the ice box was a tray to collect the water as the ice slowly melted away, evidence of its sacrifice to keep our perishables safe. If the tray wasn't emptied every day, it would overflow onto the floor. People often said, "Show me someone with rotten floorboards in the kitchen, and I'll show you someone who doesn't empty the tray under the ice box."

Because refrigeration was so primitive back then, most people in towns and cities bought their food each day. It wasn't difficult, as there were many small markets in and around the neighborhood. The grocery store across from our house was Nestler's. The meat market was Dietrich and Martin's, offering a large assortment of chops, roasts, and ground meats. They eventually opened a bakery offering German pastries and confections. Then a little farther up the street was Deneco's, which carried everything from cold cuts to canned goods—a typical neighborhood store.

Sometimes we would walk down to Union Square, where yet another assortment of businesses offered their commodities. We would head down Union Street to Church Street, then over Gate Street to Charles Street, and finally back to Clover Street. It was a large town square

TOM SERINO

with many small businesses, including Filoia's Grocery Store, which offered all the Italian items: lunch meat, cheeses, macaroni, olives, and more. Two doors down was Red's Barber Shop. Red was also a Filoia, the son of the grocer. Farther down was Barney's, a sweet shop boasting a soda fountain that was popular with the young people. There were other small grocers, bakeries, and taverns too. Virtually anything we needed was within walking distance of our house.

During the growing season, men would come around the neighborhood with their pushcarts selling fresh vegetables. The variety would change according to the time of year. In springtime you could hear the men calling out for asparagus, kale, spring peas, and cauliflower. In the early summer the blueberries, raspberries, and strawberries would appear. By midsummer there were offerings of corn, tomatoes, and melons. The men would walk slowly down the street pushing their carts and singing out the assortment of fruits or vegetables as a virtuoso sings a beloved aria.

Upon hearing their greetings, housewives would call from open windows or hurry down to the street to make their selections. Of course, this included the lighthearted bantering over freshness and price. April marked the beginning of the shad run on the Hudson River, which subsequently led to the appearance of the fish man with his pushcart and associated musical composition, "Shad! Fresh shad!"

There were no frozen foods because no one had a way to keep the items frozen. In the late summer, my mother used to can tomatoes and fruit. It was a big job, and we owned no fans or air conditioning, so our house was extremely hot during and after the process. The tomatoes were purchased fresh and then scalded and peeled. She

12

then boiled the jars and lids and hot packed the tomatoes into the sterilized jars, making sure that the lids were tightly placed to guarantee a proper seal.

The final step was to invert the jars and allow them to stand upside down to prove that the seal was airtight. That part always scared me because I was afraid the tomatoes would come rushing out of the jar and all over the counter-top; this never occurred, but the possibility was always present. Although we had little in the way of refrigeration, canning allowed us to eat everything fresh.

After dinner, my father dutifully emptied the tray of water under the ice box so my mother could rest assured that the floorboards would remain intact. Kay and I helped clean the kitchen, wiping the dishes dry before placing them back in the cupboard to await the next meal. When the kitchen was scoured to my mother's satisfaction, we were free to retreat to the living room and listen to our favorite programs on the radio.

Depending on the night of the week, we would listen to Fred Allen or Red Skelton, or maybe an adventure show like *The Green Hornet* or *The Shadow*, whose introduction never failed to frighten me. There were also dramas and variety shows. It was nice to relax in front of the radio and imagine the scenes being played out.

Soon it was time to prepare for bed. My sister and I would take turns in the bathroom, which included a sink, a bathtub, and a commode. Our former apartment had only a toilet, and the bathtub and the sink were in the hallway to be shared with two other apartments. Even at the ages of fifteen and seventeen, Kay and I slept in the same bed as we had done our entire lives.

My sister and I were very close, and still are today even in our eighties. We never had a fight. I know this seems hard to believe, but it's true. I guess when we were little, it was because I was the one who used to give in to her will. She used to like to play school. I wanted a turn to be the teacher, but Kay always insisted that she had to be the teacher. I did what she said, or she wouldn't play with me.

Now that I think of it, there was one time when we had words with each other. It was during the war, and buying a pair of stockings was nearly impossible then. The government was using the nylon to make parachutes. Because stockings were so difficult to find, some women would paint a brown line down the back of their legs so that it appeared as though they were wearing stockings.

Occasionally, Miles Shoe Store on Main Street would get a shipment of stockings, but they allowed one pair per customer. Kay and I would go up, stand in line for what seemed like an eternity, and each purchase one pair of nylon stockings. I was very cautious with mine, but Kay was rather careless with hers.

One evening, Kay had a date and she wanted to borrow my stockings. I had only one pair left, so I refused. Besides, Kay's feet were a size seven while mine were a size five.

"No, you can't wear my stockings," I said. "Your feet are bigger than mine and you'll tear them."

"No, I won't," she insisted. "I promise I won't tear them."

She begged and nagged me until I finally relented. "You can borrow my stockings. But don't tear them!"

"I won't!" So, Kay went out dancing, and when she came home, the entire front of the stocking was torn away. I was so angry with her. I suppose that's the only real disagreement we ever had.

As I crawled into bed that night after my trip to the library and Ida's, I was thankful for my sister and our large woolen blanket, for although it was late spring, the evenings were still cool. I snuggled up close to her, avoiding her cold feet that she loved to place on my legs. I was ready for a good night's sleep and the long walk to school tomorrow, and wondered who would be walking with us.

A sudden chill came over me. *What if that Tommy Serino is there tomorrow?* I thought. *What will I do? Well, maybe he won't be there, and even if he is I can just ignore him. He's too much of a wise guy for me.*

TWO

The Walk to School

The air was crisp and clean as the morning sun rose and the sounds of the neighborhood awakening filtered through our open bedroom window. My eyes were heavy even after a full night's sleep and refused to cooperate with the beautiful scenario the day was presenting to me. This was certainly not my time of day. While I loved wriggling into bed at night and snuggling under the warm covers for a blessed sleep, the experience of rising in the morning was quite the opposite. I appreciated the beautiful morning, but the motivation to begin the day remained quite absent.

Kay was already awake and dressed and was carefully arranging her hair as if the first prize in the Miss America contest was awaiting her. I slowly began my morning routine. It was my turn to make our bed, then I headed to the bathroom to get ready. My last task was to comb out and coif my short brown hair in the same manner as I did every other morning.

I could hear my mother in the kitchen. She had been up

for several hours already, preparing breakfast and lunch for my father before his long walk to the factory. Now she would have tea and hard rolls for Kay and me. Very little coffee had been available since the war. If we were fortunate, we might have some jelly left from the stock Mom made last summer.

We carried our lunches in tins that not too long before had housed Christmas cookies. Lunch was light, consisting of a wedge of homemade bread or a hard roll with a few slices of Italian lunchmeat from Filoia's, chunks of cheese, maybe some olives or peppers in oil, and whatever fruit was in season. This time of year, dried figs had to suffice.

After gathering our things, Kay and I walked up Union Street to join the gang at the candy store. My sister, who was friends with everyone, walked slightly ahead of me and reached the group first. This week she had eyes for Jimmy Reevey, so she singled him out of the crowd and walked beside him, chatting incessantly all the way.

Eugene Shurbon approached me and asked permission to carry my books. This, of course, required me to walk alongside him until we reached the school. I didn't mind. Eugene was a nice boy from a good family, and I knew he liked me. Even though I counted him a good friend, I never thought of him beyond that.

"How are you today, Doris?" Eugene asked as we began the trek to Poughkeepsie High School on North Hamilton Street.

"I'm fine, Eugene," I answered, unsure of what more I could add to the comment.

"Did you have any trouble with the math problems that Mrs. Davis assigned this week?" Eugene continued, attempting to keep our conversation going.

"Oh, I always have trouble with math," I said. "Anything beyond two plus two is out of reach for me." I generally had difficulty in school, although I did believe that if a teacher would just take a little time to explain things in a manner that I could understand, I might grasp the concepts more quickly.

"I know what you mean," Eugene said, interrupting my thoughts, "I have real problems in English. Oh, I speak it all right, but the way it's put together is far beyond me."

"Hey, Eugene! Whatcha doing?"

When I turned at hearing the voice, Tommy Serino had appeared from out of nowhere.

"Oh, hi, Doris," he said to me. "How are you?" Then he looked at Eugene. "Hey, Gene, did you see that catch I made last night when Bobby hit that pop fly into center field? I thought I was going right through the pizza stand window. But I got it and we won the game." He glanced at me. "You should have seen it, Doris."

I didn't respond. He was such a showoff.

"Hey, you girls should come and watch us play sometime. We're playing basketball this Saturday afternoon at Lincoln Center. I think Kay has been there before with some of the other girls."

I didn't mean to be rude, but I really had no intention of going to watch him show off. "I don't think so. I'll be with my family on Saturday."

"Oh. Okay, then," he said. "Maybe we'll see you at the dance tomorrow night. I heard the LaFalce brothers are playing there again this week. You're going, right, Eugene?"

Eugene muttered something inaudible while I responded, "I doubt it."

Tommy looked at me. "Oh. I thought Kay said that you guys were going. Okay, then. Well, I hope to see you there. Bye, Gene." And off he went. He was persistent.

The remainder of the walk to school was rather quiet. Eugene couldn't seem to maintain much conversation, and I was simply annoyed at the impertinence of Tommy Serino. When we arrived at the high school, Eugene handed my books to me, muttered that he hoped to see me at lunchtime, and then disappeared. I took a deep breath and slowly climbed the steps, headed for my first class.

I didn't like school at all. Classroom study was difficult for me, and even the simple concepts of math and English were confusing. History was a little more interesting, but it was virtually impossible to memorize all the names and dates. I never felt that the teachers were clear in their explanations and sometimes even wondered if we were speaking the same language.

Kay, on the other hand, was very intelligent and schoolwork came easy to her. When trying to help me with my homework, she would become impatient at my inability to grasp concepts she deemed quite elementary, and I would simply give up.

When I was in the fifth grade, I had a teacher named Mrs. Hayes. One evening, the school hosted an open house where parents could discuss their children's progress. My mother was talking to Mrs. Hayes, who sternly declared to my mother, "Doris is not another Kay. She could be if she tried, but she doesn't try." What Mrs. Hayes failed to recognize was that I was putting forth my best effort but learning in a classroom setting didn't come naturally to me. On the contrary, it eluded me rather efficiently. After hearing this from the teacher, I simply refused to apply myself.

When I started high school, I'd hoped for a better experience. Kay had taken the secretarial course of study, and the first year consisted of all introductory business courses. This was what I wanted, because only certain jobs were available to women back then and nursing and teaching were of no interest to me. I went to the guidance counselor at the start of high school to establish my course of study for the next four years, but there were so many girls enrolled in the secretarial program that there were few openings in the classes, and the upper classmen were registered first.

Consequently, my guidance counselor simply filled my schedule with an assortment of disparate subjects. My first year of high school consisted of subjects unrelated to the secretarial program: history of antiques, cooking, business math, and ancient history. As the year progressed, I became increasingly more frustrated and even contemplated dropping out, but to do so I needed parental permission. I decided to finish the year and discuss my future with my parents another time.

The day passed swiftly, and on the walk home Eugene was much more garrulous. With no sign of Tommy Serino, Eugene could talk without interruption. The gang arrived at the candy store, and Kay wanted to spend a little more time with Jimmy before going home.

Eugene had to leave for his after-school job at the meat market. He would clean the back room, make whatever deliveries were lingering from the day, and sweep the front service area before heading home. But he needed to hurry to be on time. Mr. Dietrich, the owner, did not appreciate tardiness. I decided to wait for Kay, and if necessary to prompt her if the hour grew late.

I enjoyed listening to the boys' playful banter. It was quite amusing. Then I heard the bell on the candy store door sound as the door was opened, and when I turned, Tommy Serino and John DelSanto were descending the steps.

"Hi, Doris," Tommy said when our eyes met. "Nice to see you again."

"Where were you at the end of school today?" I asked, sounding more maternal than expected.

He walked toward me. "I skipped the last couple of classes today. School ends in less than two weeks, so they aren't really covering anything important anyway. Where's Eugene?"

"He left for work at Dietrich and Martin's."

"So, what are you doing here?" Tommy asked.

"I'm just waiting for my sister." I shrugged. "There's no homework since it's so close to the end of the school year."

"Yeah. You want a piece of my Mars bar?" Tommy was really trying to be friendly.

"No, thank you," I answered shyly.

"Hey, are you thinking about going to the dance at Canon Street tomorrow night? The LaFalce brothers have a ten-piece orchestra and they're really good."

"I don't know, Tommy," I said. "My family usually goes out together on Friday nights. I'll have to see what my mother says. I can only say maybe."

He grinned. "Well, that's good enough for me." And with that he was gone.

I turned to Kay and told her that we needed to be going before Mom got upset with us for being late getting home. She reluctantly came down from the stoop, and we quickened our pace when the chimes on the old Nativity Church rang four o'clock.

THREE

The Weekend

H urry up, girls. Let's get these groceries away and the table set for dinner." My mother immediately began taking command as we entered the house. Our Friday night routine was structured and predictable, just as every other aspect of daily life with my mother. After school, when my dad would get home from work, my family would walk up to Main Street to do our weekly shopping for non-perishables at the A&P. We each would carry home a bag or two of household essentials generally amounting to a total of six dollars, one-tenth of my dad's weekly salary.

Once everything was properly relegated to its specific location in the kitchen, Mom began to prepare dinner. It was Friday, so no meat was allowed. Instead, we were served a steaming bowl of pasta fagioli with a wedge of Italian bread on the side.

My mother was a wonderful cook and could seemingly create dinner from the sparsest of ingredients. Every week we had soup of some variety, usually made from whatever vegetables were available. Potatoes were a staple for us.

Mom would often fry them with peppers, sausage, tomatoes, etc. If not potatoes, then eggs were scrambled with peppers, chicory, or some Italian lunchmeats. Friday was always meatless, so dinner consisted of beans and macaroni, peas and macaroni, or, if Daddy went fishing, fried fish from the Hudson River. Sunday dinner was a work of art. Mom would make a roast, if it was available, or her Sunday sauce made with pork neck bones, meatballs, and sausage. The sauce was started early in the morning and cooked all day, leaving its heavenly aroma lingering throughout the house well into the night.

This Friday night, like most others, my parents were going to their friends' house to play dominos. I had known Hattie and Albert since I was five years old. They lived across the street from us when we moved to Poughkeepsie in 1938. They were lifelong friends of my parents, and never had any children, so they treated Kay and me like family. Albert would make a special hot chocolate with whipped marshmallow and tell us all kinds of wonderful stories, swearing that they were all absolutely true. Then while the grownups were playing dominos, Kay and I would listen to the radio until we fell asleep on the couch, and Daddy would carry us home across the street one at a time.

But we were older now, and Kay was often out on a date on Friday night. I would sometimes accompany her as a chaperone, a job which neither of us appreciated. Tonight was different. Both of us wanted to go to the dance on Canon Street. It seemed that everyone we knew would be there. So, with just the smallest amount of coercion from us, my mother permitted us to go.

After we cleaned up the kitchen following dinner, Kay was the first one in the bathroom, which left me with minimal time to prepare. This resulted in us leaving late, which was of course my fault. We met the gang at the candy store and started the walk to the Masonic Lodge.

I quickly noticed that mostly girls were walking with us tonight. Some of the boys were already at the dance. It was a warm evening, so when we arrived on Canon Street, the doors of the lodge were open and the music was spilling out into the night air. Inside, we were enveloped by the soft strains of "Moonlight Serenade" played expertly by the LaFalce brothers.

Kay found Jimmy Reevey and they went out onto the dance floor. No one would be a wallflower tonight. Everyone was there to dance. Some of the girls actually carried dance cards and wrote down the names of the young men who asked for a dance. Many wanted to dance with every fellow who wasn't already attached to one girl.

Dancing was popular in 1948, and dances were held in various places all weekend. The YMCA hosted a dance every Saturday night, while the local churches often opened their doors to young people to dance and play records on Friday evenings.

At Nativity Church on Union Street, the monsignor's housekeeper, Miss Tilly, would open the doors at eight in the evening and set her alarm clock for eleven o'clock. The Hungarian church hall would open the doors if a suitable chaperone was available. My mother would frequently come and chaperone a dance there on Saturday nights while my dad and his friends were gathered at the house.

Several boys asked me to dance that night. Of course, Eugene was there. He danced with me several times, but when he went to get me a cup of fruit punch, Tommy Serino approached.

"Hi, Doris! Let's dance."

As usual he was rather abrupt in his approach, but I agreed, and we went out on the dance floor. Tommy was a mediocre dancer, and he was always fooling around and attempting fancy moves and confusing me. He was such a showoff. Yet some of his antics did make me laugh in spite of myself.

Suddenly the music slowed down, and rather than walk off the dance floor, Tommy reached out and pulled me close. He was gentle and smooth when he danced slowly, quite the contrast from his previous actions. I was listening closely to the song the LaFalce brothers were playing "You Can't be True, Dear" when Tommy asked, "Can I walk you home tonight?"

This request took me aback, and I was at a loss for words.

"Is anyone walking you home tonight?" he went on. "If not, I'd like to see you to your door."

"Well, I guess that will be okay. I mean, I came with Kay and the girls, but, I mean, we all leave at the same time anyway," I stammered.

"Okay, then. Great. Save the last dance for me."

And with that, the song ended. I danced with several other boys that night, but when the band announced the last dance, there was Tommy. He took my hand and we walked out on the dance floor and ended the night dancing to the Charioteer's "It's Too Soon to Know."

As the dance ended, the lights came up and everyone began walking toward the front doors. Our gang began to gather outside around the front steps. I looked for Kay, but she was nowhere in sight. So Tommy and I began strolling down Canon Street toward Union Street.

He talked about his favorite music, the songs from that night, and whether the LaFalce brothers had played them well or not. All the time I was listening to him, I was oblivious to the others walking with us.

As we made our way down Union Street, Tommy asked, "Do you want to grab a soda at Barney's?"

"I'd better not," I said. "My parents will be home by now and waiting for me."

"Okay." A few minutes later, he stopped. "Well, here's your house."

I looked at him. "How do you know where I live?" I'd never mentioned it before.

Tommy laughed. "I used to live in the house right behind you, on Church Street. That fence along the back of your yard? That was our fence."

Wow, I'd never known he was that close! "When did you live there?" I asked.

"We moved from there to where I live now on Jefferson Street when I was ten. So it's been a while." Tommy smiled. "Will I see you tomorrow?"

"Tomorrow?" I couldn't remember having any plans for the next day.

"Yeah, we're playing basketball at Lincoln Center tomorrow afternoon. I'd like you to come."

I detected a tinge of pleading in his request. "I'll have to see what my mother says. Tomorrow's cleaning day at my house."

He laughed. "We never have those at my house. But we'll be there at three. I hope you can make it. G'night."

"Bye, Tommy," I said softly.

When I entered the house, Daddy was waiting in the living room. "How was the dance?" he asked.

"It was fun," I answered. *But the walk home was even better,* I thought.

"Where's Catherine?" Daddy always called my sister by her full name.

"I don't know. I didn't see her when the dance ended."

His expression sobered. "Did you walk home by yourself, then?"

"No, Daddy," I assured him. "I walked with the rest of the girls, and one of the boys walked me to my door."

Dad looked at me pensively for only a moment, but it seemed rather invasive. "I see. And which boy might that be?"

"Tommy Serino. He lives over on Jefferson Street."

"I know the Serinos. Thank him for me when you see him again."

"I will, Daddy." Knowing that my father's concerns had been satisfied, for now, I kissed him goodnight and went to my bedroom. Hopefully I would be in bed before Kay got home.

FOUR

Saturday

I got no extra sleep on Saturday morning. Mom was up
bright and early, and the colossal cleaning of the entire
house was about to begin. There was no compromise with
the enemies of domiciliary hygiene in our house. If cleanli-
ness was next to godliness, my mother was most certainly in
line for sainthood.

After a quick breakfast, we began the process in our
bedroom. All bed linens were stripped and replaced with
fresh bedding. The used linens would be washed and hung
out to dry on Monday, then folded and placed in the closet
to await their turn to cover our beds once again. The floor
would be swept, and all horizontal surfaces dusted. It was
Kay's turn to clean the bathroom, which included scrubbing the sink, toilet, tub, and floor.

She was not moving quickly this morning, indicative of
a late arrival last night and vigorous inquisition by anticipating parents. Kay was an independent spirit and didn't
always appreciate the safeguards that came with obedience
to parental regulations. This often resulted in lively encoun-

ters, especially with Mom. Whatever the result of last night's confrontation, Kay was definitely approaching her chores prudently.

While Kay was occupied in the bathroom, I collected all the rugs in the house and carried them outside to the clothesline, where they were beaten into submission to Mom's standard of purity. There were hooked rugs, tied rugs made of rags, small oval rugs near the beds to warm our feet on cold mornings, and one large rectangular rug in the parlor that required Daddy's assistance to carry outside and hoist up on the line. A broomstick was then used to strike the rug, and the airborne particles of dirt were free to travel the neighborhood in search of another household carpet in which to find rest.

With the carpets hanging securely from the clothesline, it was time to sweep all the floors in the house. Bedrooms, hallway, bathroom, parlor, and kitchen—no room was neglected, and every particle of dust was evicted. Only then would rugs be returned to their positions on the floor in each room.

Dad was about to leave for the market to buy some supplies for the festivities that night. On Saturday nights, my dad's brothers and friends would come from Newburgh: Uncle Angelo, Uncle Pete, and Uncle Carmine, as well as some friends with unusual nicknames such as LuJohn and Dooda. These men would gather at our house to play "fingers," actually called *mora*, a Sicilian hand game where bets were placed on which number would appear from the combination of fingers displayed by two opponents.

My dad would do all the cooking—meatballs or sausage and peppers on wedges of Italian bread, Italian meats and cheeses for sandwiches, fresh roasted peppers, and hot peppers in oil. The men would be there until late at night drinking beer and wine and eating and playing "fingers." The longer they played, the more they drank and the louder they became.

Kay and I frequently attended the dances on Saturday nights at the Hungarian hall, and my mother found it a convenient escape to chaperone those dances. When we arrived home, the men were still going strong. They were always happy to see us and greeted us warmly and loudly, offering us wine or beer, and summoning my mother's strict scolding. This always solicited uproarious laughter and a return to their game.

Before Dad could make his departure to the market that day, my mother called from the kitchen, where she had just finished scrubbing the floor, "Joe, come in here and empty the ice box tray. I don't want it to overflow on my clean floor."

"I'll do it when I get back," Dad replied.

"Do it now!" my mother insisted.

"Awww! *Sta fimina m'a fa pazzu!*"

"Never mind that," my mother retorted." Just get in here and empty the tray."

"I'm coming," he grumbled.

This wasn't an unusual dialogue between my parents. They never really disagreed on anything. My father adored my mother and would do anything for her. He accepted the fact that she was regimented and unyielding in her routines and nothing was going to interfere with her schedule. But he was willing to accept this quirk for the sake of a tidy and ordered home. Every so often he felt the need to assert his dominance verbally, to which my mother's response was always contrary. Yet, in important matters concerning the family, she would yield to his decisions.

Around two in the afternoon, we finished our chores.

After a quick lunch, Kay and I prepared to go to Lincoln Center where the boys were playing basketball. As we walked up Union Street to Jefferson Street, I asked her, "Where did you disappear after the dance last night?"

"Jimmy and I went up to Market Street to see if the Bardavon had a late movie," she said.

"Did they?"

"No. So we walked down to Union Square and then down to the river to sit for a while."

"Did you get home late?" I asked, already knowing the answer.

"It wasn't that late. Mom always makes such a big deal out of what time I come home. I'll be eighteen in nine months. She needs to start treating me more like a grown-up."

Kay's friends Irma Patera, Margaret Waligora, and Kate Tokosh greeted us as we approached the corner of Union and Jefferson Streets. "Hi, girls." Margaret chimed, "We'll be late for the game if we don't hurry." As we all walked, they chattered about boys, clothes, makeup, and other superfluous subjects of which I had little interest.

Soon we were approaching the corner of Pine and Montgomery Streets and I could see the Lincoln Center. It was a large, old building that had been completely refurbished in 1937 as part of President Roosevelt's Works Progress Administration. Outside, the grounds were well kept, practically manicured. There were swings and a tetherball court, as well as a large baseball field behind the building, which was in use this afternoon by some colored boys from another part of town.

Young people from all over the city came to the center, especially on weekends. During the summer months, sports leagues were formed, arts and crafts classes were offered,

TOM SERINO

and concerts and dances were hosted. During the week there were night classes for those working to attain their citizenship or to improve their English. Inside, the Lincoln Center boasted a full-sized gymnasium complete with locker rooms and showers.

Today was Saturday, so the gym was open for neighborhood kids to play, and Tommy and the boys were already there. As Margaret had predicted, the game had just started. Tommy glanced over at us as we climbed the steps to the top row of the three rows of bleachers. The teams seemed evenly matched and the game was rather fast paced. Tommy couldn't play a serious game though, instead joking around on the court. He tapped the opposing player on the right shoulder, and as he turned, Tommy dribbled the ball around his left side and made the basket. The next time Tommy had the ball he made a fast break for the net. But as he was going up for the layup instead of making the basket, he passed the ball to a waiting Billy Reevey, who was unguarded and made the basket with ease. There was lots of shouting and calling out.

Margaret thought he was the funniest and cutest guy and laughed uncontrollably at his exploits. I had to admit that some of his horseplay was quite humorous, and he seemed a capable athlete.

After the game, we met the boys on the court. One team said they had won, while the other team claimed victory for themselves. It didn't really matter to anyone, though. It was all for fun.

"When you went up for that layup and passed the ball to Billy, I was so surprised," Margaret told Tommy. "Why, I thought I'd seen everything until then."

"Thanks, Margaret," Tommy said, then looked at me. "What did you think, Doris?"

I blushed a little for being put on the spot, but gathered myself enough to reply, "It was a fun game."

"Did you see when I stole the ball from that guy and made the basket. That put us ahead in the game and we never lost the lead."

I wasn't so sure about that, as there was some discrepancy over the final score, but I wasn't going to argue. "I saw that."

"We're going to get changed and go down to Barney's," Tommy told us. "You girls going to come?"

"Of course we are," Margaret said. "Aren't we, Doris?"

I tried to smile. "I suppose so."

As we walked down to Barney's, Margaret prattled on about school, what she would be doing this summer, and how much she liked watching the boys play sports. I stayed quiet, listening to the chatter and the boys bantering over who was the best player and whose effort won the game for the team. It was funny to hear them compare themselves to famous basketball players, none of whom were familiar to me.

At Barney's, Margaret and Kate went to the ladies' room while Kay and Irma sat in a booth with room for the boys. I sat on a stool at the soda fountain, and Tommy sat next to me.

"What can I get for you, Doris?" he asked.

"Oh, I'll have a Cherry Coke, I guess."

Tommy ordered a Cherry Coke for me and a chocolate Coke for himself.

Margaret and Kate came back, and Margaret didn't seem overly concerned that I was talking to Tommy. She and Kate started talking with Bernie Wisocki and Bobby Heller.

"So did you like the game?" Tommy asked as I sipped my Cherry Coke.

"Yes. It was exciting to watch."

"We usually play every weekend. Sometimes we play football in the field across the street at Eastman Park, or baseball in the yard down near the hospital. You know, the one on Lincoln Avenue."

"Oh, yes," I said.

"During the summer, we go to Greenvale Farms out on Route 376," he continued. "There's a swimming hole there and a big, open field. There are picnic benches, and we spend the whole day there."

"How do you get out there?" I asked. "There are no buses that run in that direction."

"Frank Bitzko has a car, and we go when he has off from work. You should come with us sometime this summer. I know that you'd like it."

It did sound like a lot of fun, but of course I would have to put this idea by my mother first.

He swallowed. "So, Doris, um, do you want to go to the movies with me next Friday night? *Red River* is playing at the Bardavon Theatre. You know, the one with John Wayne and Montgomery Clift. Then after that is a vaudeville show. I think you'd like it. What do you say?"

I was astonished. I'd known Tommy only a short time, and he was asking me for a date. While I was still uncertain about him, some things about Tommy really appealed to me. He was comical and entertaining, and time spent with him was never dull. Yet, even though he talked a great deal, he seemed a difficult person to really get to know. I supposed that spending time with just him, I might get to know him better. "Yes, I would like that," I said.

A broad smile spread across Tommy's face, and he took

a sip of his chocolate Coke. "Okay, then. I'll pick you up at your house next Friday at seven thirty."

"Fine," I replied.

Later that afternoon as our group walked home, we dropped off individuals at their prospective street. Tommy talked to just me the entire time, and as the next street neared, he abruptly said, "My house is around the corner. I'll see you at school this week, and don't forget about Friday night."

"Okay," I said, a little confused by his haste. I wasn't really sure precisely where he lived. He always seemed to disappear before anyone approached his house.

Kay and I were among the last of the gang to depart. We reached the end of Union Street and bid everyone goodbye, then turned the corner onto South Clover Street, where we lived. We would see most of the gang at mass tomorrow morning.

As we entered the house, we were greeted by the aroma of meatballs and sausage in tomato sauce coming from the kitchen. My mother had escaped to Hattie's for the evening, and my dad was cooking for his gang, who would be arriving within the hour. Kay and I sat in the kitchen, and Daddy served us some meatballs on a wedge of Italian bread. He was an incredible cook, and his meatballs were a work of art.

Kay was going out with Jimmy again tonight, so I was left to help Daddy serve his guests. I enjoyed being around my uncles, and they were always good to me. Whoever was winning the games tonight would be certain to slip me several dollars. If it was Uncle Carmine, I would surely receive double that. I was his favorite, and he pulled no bones about telling everyone. He had been there the day I was born and, in his own words, when he first laid eyes on me, he said, "I looked in the crib and there you were. You were my little girl from that day on."

When I was young, Uncle Carmine would come to Poughkeepsie and take me out on a "date." We would walk up the street hand in hand and go to the movies or to a soda shop. He was a sharp dresser, always wearing beautiful clothes, and was an incredibly handsome man. I guess he was my favorite too.

The men began to arrive as I was putting wine and cold beer on the table. The Italian bread had been cut into wedges and sliced open for sandwiches, and Daddy put the pot in the middle of the table for easy access to all. Trays of deli meats from Filoia's—capicola, soprasatta, mortadella, and salami—and deli cheeses, provolone, and "soft cheese" (our term for the soft mozzarella in water) spread across the table. Jars of peppers in oil were opened, and the feast was about to begin.

All the men arrived at the same time since they came together in Uncle Pete's car. As my uncles entered one by one, they all greeted me with hugs and kisses. Then Uncle Carmine came in and exclaimed, "There's my little girl!" and picked me up, swung me around, and kissed me.

"Uncle Carm! I'm not a little girl anymore," I protested.

With mock sternness, he firmly declared, "You'll always be my little girl, honey."

LuJohn and Dooda came in carrying several bottles of homemade wine and at least three pepperoni that I could count. The men attacked the table as if a famine had been declared for tomorrow, filling glasses of wine and dipping wedges of Italian bread into the sauce. I went into the kitchen to grab some washcloths for the men to wipe their hands (after all, you can't play "fingers" with greasy hands!).

As I reentered the dining room, Uncle Pete said, "Hey, Doris, are you married yet?"

I flushed bright red. "Uncle Pete! I'm only fifteen."

"Yes, but you'll be sixteen soon, and there'll be a young boy coming around with the wolf in his eye!"

The men all laughed, but Uncle Carmine came to my defense. "Some guy comes after my little girl, and I'll kick his *culo* all over town."

I gave him a quick "thank you" smile and retreated into the kitchen.

The men soon began their games, and I could hear them calling out numbers in Italian as I was busy washing dirty plates and glasses and refilling plates with food. As the hour grew later, my dad called me to him and took me gently around the waist. "You should get ready for bed now, sweetie. I can take over until your mom gets home. Thanks for all your help."

"You're welcome, Daddy," I said.

I really loved helping my dad, and I loved being around my uncles. I gave each one a kiss goodnight, and of course each one slipped me some cash. As I retired to the bedroom to begin my nighttime routine, I heard my mother come in. She immediately began scolding the men for talking so loudly that they could be heard from down the street. Now things would be in perfect order, for stability and solidity had entered the house in the person of Alice Messina.

FIVE

Summer of 1948

I was exceptionally tired after a busy weekend, so Monday arrived like an unwelcomed guest. I trudged through my morning routine preparing for school so I could attend classes I completely despised. My mood was one of increasing melancholy functioning with a lack of enthusiasm that would rival a man taking the long walk to the gallows. The only redeeming factor was that this was the last week of school and the long summer lay ahead with much promise.

As Kay and I walked out our apartment door, I turned to say goodbye to my mother, who was busy at the kitchen sink washing the bed linens we had changed on Saturday. "See you later, Mom."

She called back to us without looking up, "You girls be good!"

As we exited the building to my great surprise, Tommy Serino stood there on the sidewalk. "Hi, Doris," he said cheerfully. "How are you doing?

"What are you doing here?" I asked, my surprise sounding more terse than I intended.

"I, uh, wanted to walk you to school this morning. Is that okay with you?"

I softened my tone. "Sorry, Tommy. I'm just really tired this morning."

"That's all right. Here, let me carry your books."

I handed them over, my mood brightening slightly. I was genuinely pleased to see him and how jovial he was on an early Monday morning.

We met up with the rest of the gang at the candy store and started the long walk to North Hamilton Street.

"You're graduating next year, right, Tommy?" I asked him. I already knew that he was—he was in the same class as Kay—but it seemed like a nice way to open the conversation.

"Yeah."

"Well, what will you do after that?" I inquired when he didn't say any more.

"I don't know for sure. I'll probably work with my dad and apprentice as a bricklayer. After the apprenticeship I'll either work with him or maybe join the union. I'm not sure exactly, but I know I couldn't stand working in a factory. Inside work isn't for me." He looked at me. "How about you? You still have a couple of years of school left, right?"

"I'm not sure yet either," I confessed. "I wanted to get into the secretarial program, but I can't get the classes I need. I'm thinking of dropping out and going to work with my dad at the factory." I had never revealed this to anyone before and found it remarkable that I was sharing this with him. "I need to find the proper time to speak with my parents about it."

Tommy seemed genuinely interested in me and offered

his encouragement. "Well, if you're not getting what you want in school, it might be wise to learn another skill that can earn you some money."

I nodded. "I just don't know how my parents are going to react. I'm a little afraid to approach the subject with them."

"Well, you might be surprised. They probably suspect your feelings already."

Tommy's words amazed me. They seemed to have genuine wisdom, and they definitely made me feel better about talking to my parents. "Thanks, Tommy," I said. "You're right. I shouldn't put it off any longer."

Soon we arrived at school. The walk seemed to have passed so quickly this morning.

Tommy handed my books to me. "I'll see you after school, okay?"

"Bye, Tommy," I replied.

The school day dragged on, with each hour seeming to last much longer than sixty minutes. I was anticipating the walk home with Tommy, and when the last bell rang, I hurried outside to where the gang was gathering for the trek home.

I watched as one by one the gang gathered and soon, we were ready to begin the long walk to Union Street. But Tommy was nowhere in sight. I looked all around, and there was no sign of him anywhere. As the gang began to move in the direction of home, I realized that Tommy wasn't coming. I walked alone, hearing nothing but the muffled sounds of conversations in which I had no part.

Tommy had led me to believe that he would be waiting for me after school and walk me home. He had obviously stood me up. With my thoughts accusing him and excusing him simultaneously, I fought and contended with him in my mind. I was embarrassed that I'd trusted him and furious that he'd proven to be unworthy of that trust.

By the time we reached the candy store, I was livid. My outrage was ready to be unfurled without restraint the next time I saw him—and that opportunity came sooner than expected.

"Hi, Doris," Tommy's voice said from behind me as I stood on the steps of the candy store.

I ignored him.

"How was school?"

"Where were you?" I spat back at him.

Tommy recoiled. "What do you mean?"

"You said that you would meet me after school. I waited for you, and you didn't show up. Why did you lie to me?"

Tommy's expression darkened. "I said that I'd see you after school. I didn't say that I would meet you after school. It's after school now and I'm seeing you."

"Don't play with me, Tommy Serino," I said, giving vent to the full measure of my fury. "You misled me, and now you're pretending you did nothing wrong."

"You're being too sensitive, Doris." Tommy tried, in vain, to smooth things over.

"Don't even talk to me right now, okay?" I said, unwavering in my indignation.

"Fine!" He turned and left without another word.

As I watched him walk away, a myriad of conflicting emotions bombarded my mind. I was glad that I had addressed Tommy's callous arrogance and complete lack of consideration. At the same time, I was sad that I'd obviously hurt his feelings. Then I was also embarrassed that he had stood me up and angry that he refused to admit any fault in his actions. Tommy Serino was an unusual person, an enigma in many ways, and extremely hard to understand.

Little did I realize that this was the direction our relationship would take over the next two years. We would be together and have a wonderful time relating to one another —and then we would fight over something insignificant, and Tommy would go his way and I would go mine. We would even date other people, but invariably we would end up back together.

We did go to the movies that Friday night—after Tommy admitted that although he didn't lie, he didn't communicate very well. We had an enjoyable evening, and spending time with him was fun. He was different, and I was determined to get to know this young man who was equally determined not to be known.

The last week of school seemed to endure for an eternity. As the week dragged on, each successive day seemed longer and more grueling than the day before. Mercifully, the end of the week came and the year finally ended. As the doors of the high school opened and the final bell signaled the termination of the 1948 school year, it was as if the gates of purgatory were unsealed and the captives set at liberty.

Summertime was now upon us. The gang would spend the three months together, and there would be something to do virtually every evening. The dances continued every Friday night at Nativity Church and every Saturday night at the Hungarian hall and the YMCA. In addition, street dances and block parties occurred in different neighborhoods at random times. Occasionally we would go roller-skating at the rink on Canon Street or take the bus to Newburgh to the large roller rink called the Avalon. If we were fortunate enough to have access to a car, we would go to Adelle's on Route 44, which like the Avalon was a large roller rink, and they featured a new type of drive-in diner complete with "curb service," where the waitresses would approach the vehicle on roller skates to take and serve your order. It was a great innovation that added something new and exciting to our social experience.

Several times over the summer, our gang had the opportunity to drive out to Greenvale Farms and enjoy a picnic and bathing in the swimming hole. On one particular outing, having spent the entire afternoon and evening at the park, as darkness enveloped the grove, two of the guys took off their clothes and went skinny dipping in the pool. The moment they were in the water, the other fellows seized the opportunity and took all their clothes and tied them to a tree.

When the naturist swimmers came out of the water, two cars were facing them as they struggled to free their clothes from the tree. The cars simultaneously turned on their headlights and began blowing their car horns, illuminating the two young men in all their primal glory and drawing the attention of every person in the vicinity. Surely the roar of laughter emanating from the crowd could be heard in Midtown Manhattan.

Poughkeepsie was bustling with activity that summer. The municipal swimming pools were overflowing with bathers. The city parks were crowded with weekend picnics and sandlot sporting events. It seemed that the entire populace was bursting with relief and levity after decades of Depression and war. People were ready to celebrate, and the general mood that summer was festive.

In June and July were the Feast of Saint Anthony and the Feast of Our Lady of Mount Carmel hosted by Mount

Carmel church. These were two-day festivals that closed off several blocks surrounding Mount Carmel Square. Festivities began with a procession of the statue of the corresponding saint around the block, followed by a host of the faithful, many of whom were barefoot. Parishioners and sightseers would cast coins on the bier, or pin one-, five- and ten-dollar bills to the robes that adorned the saintly effigy.

The larger the denomination of cash, the greater the piety reflected by the faithful, and the larger the favor silently requested from the saintly intercessor. After the procession, a mass in honor of the patron saint was followed by great amusements in the street.

Food vendors sold steaming sandwiches of sausage and peppers or meatballs, pizza fritta, and steamed clams with butter or marinara. Games of chance were played, where bets were placed and small fortunes were both won and lost. Carnival games abounded for children and adults alike —games of skill requiring a participant to break balloons with a dart or launch a penny into a jar or ring a bell by striking a plate with a mallet. A furry prize was awarded to the winner, and the loser received a great chiding and encouragement to try again. These festivals were highly entertaining and were well attended by people from all over the city.

There was much work to accomplish for my family during the summer months. The canning of tomatoes and peaches was a priority. But there were also times of refreshing and relaxation. Eastman Park with its fragrant pine groves had sandlot baseball games every weekend, and we would often go to watch them on a Sunday afternoon. My mother loved picnics, and we would have one almost every Sunday throughout the summer. Her favorite picnic spot was Lake Walton.

My uncle Morgan would come up from New Windsor in his old farm truck with assorted members of the family and take us out to Lake Walton for the day. Everyone would bring their picnic baskets, bathing suits, and sundry items for the day and pile into the back of the truck. It wasn't very comfortable, but no one seemed to mind. Escaping the sweltering city for the shade trees and the cool breeze coming off the water was wonderful. We would spend the entire day enjoying food, games, and the company of family and friends, and we wouldn't leave until the park closed at sundown.

Labor Day was traditionally the last picnic of the summer season. Always a big event, it was attended by as many family members and friends as possible. All my uncles and aunts from New Windsor would come, along with my mother's sister Betty, our family friends Hattie and Albert, and an assortment of others who made time to celebrate the end of summer with us. Sandwiches and salads were in abundance, as well as hamburgers and hot dogs, and sausage and peppers or meatballs on hard rolls. There was always plenty of food, and every year someone would be wrestled into submission by my uncles, then thrown into the lake with their clothes on. Fortunately, my uncles were always kind enough to avoid selecting Kay or me, knowing that we didn't know how to swim and were deathly afraid of the water.

When the day ended, there were long goodbyes with many hugs and kisses as everyone realized that we would not come together like this again until next summer. School would begin immediately after, and the summer celebrations would come to an end.

I had enrolled in my sophomore year of high school in hopes of finally obtaining the necessary courses for the secretarial program. My studies were already behind since no courses in this curriculum had been available last year, and I'd decided to see the guidance counselor early to register—hopefully—for the needed classes.

But until then I would enjoy the blissful, lazy days of summer.

SIX
The Enigma, Tommy Serino

Tommy and I spent a great deal of time together that summer. There were the usual outings with the gang, football or basketball games, and the dances each week, and we also spent time together alone. Sometimes we would take a long walk to Arlington, on the other side of the city. On the return trip we would stop at Alex's, an uptown soda fountain, to get a chocolate Coke. We went to the movies almost every Friday night—that is, when we weren't fighting.

Ours was an interesting relationship. Tommy and I continued to date, then fight and breakup, then come back together again. I would get angry with him over something he said or did or neglected to do and wouldn't speak to him. On other occasions Tommy would be upset over something I did, and he would storm off and I wouldn't see him for a while. During those times it wasn't unusual for both of us to date other people. Tommy would often date Eleanor DiPilco. Her mother and Tommy's mother were good friends and secretly wanted the two of them to marry.

Eleanor was crazy about Tommy, so she was always ready to go out with him when he came around.

Ironically, Tommy became jealous when I would date other fellows. On one occasion, after we'd broken up yet again, Tommy's friend Billy Freer asked me out on a date. I'd just bought a new dress and new shoes, and when I wore them I looked quite chic. I felt like Ava Gardner or Elizabeth Taylor.

When Billy came to pick me up, he commented on how beautiful I looked, that it was a shame we were going to the movies and the room would be dark. I blushed and took his arm, and we started to walk up Union Street. As we passed the candy store, where Tommy stood with some of the guys, he glared at us as we walked by. I refused to even look at him.

He told the other guys, "She never dressed like that for me!"

Billy and I had a good time at the movies, and when he walked me home, there was Tommy, still at the candy store. I learned later that when Billy was returning home, he reached the candy store and Tommy grabbed him and said, "Don't you dare take her out again."

In the late summer, just before school began, Tommy and I weren't together, and I began to date Sam Ciofi. He was an attractive young man with a swarthy complexion and wavy black hair. We dated quite consistently for about six weeks. I liked Sam, but I was always comparing him to Tommy. I finally broke up with him because Sam, who was eighteen years old, wanted to get serious and that was much too fast for me. Besides, I missed being with Tommy. How could someone make me so angry one minute and then I missed him so much the next minute?

Several days later, I saw Tommy on the way to school.

"Hi, Doris. How are you?" he asked.

"Fine," I responded hesitantly.

"How's Sam?"

I didn't appreciate his smart remark. "I don't really know," I said. "How's Eleanor?"

"I don't really know either," Tommy replied with a twinkle in his eye.

We stared at each other for a moment and then both burst out laughing. We talked all the way to school that morning, and all was right with the world.

During the summer our gang had been together almost every day. On Thursday nights we would gather around the radio in our parlor to enjoy a program called "Life with Luigi." The action centered on Luigi Basco and his experiences as a newly arrived Italian immigrant in Chicago. Many episodes took place at the night school classes that Luigi attended with other immigrants from different countries. Another common theme was Luigi's landlord and sponsor, Pasquale, scheming to get Luigi to marry his obese daughter, Rosa.

Anticipating the arrival of the gang, my mother would bake all day—cookies, cakes, pies, and confections of every variety. She would serve them to our friends as we listened to the radio and enjoyed each other's company. The gang was frequently at my house, and every chair, sofa and space on the floor would be occupied. Nevertheless, my mother appreciated hosting the young people in our home, as it allowed her to get to know our friends. Since Tommy was usually at these gatherings, my parents had the opportunity to become acquainted with him.

Neither of my parents were very impressed with Tommy Serino when they first met him. He was cordial, affable, and respectful, but he was pugnacious and always on the defensive. He never spoke of his family and avoided questions about them as if maneuvering through a mine field. My father kept a vigilant, protective eye on him. My mother, on the other hand, felt a certain compassion toward him. While she believed him to be brash and portraying a presumptuous pseudo-confidence, she sensed that there was a broken spirit beneath the surface of his brusque exterior.

My mother was well acquainted with childhood suffering. She and her two sisters had been orphaned when their mother died during the influenza epidemic and their father was killed in a construction accident six months later. The three little girls were left in the care of a kind, gentle-spirited grandmother and a harsh, alcoholic grandfather who became crueler with every drop of whiskey consumed. Her grandparents were Scottish Presbyterian immigrants from Ballymoney, County Antrim, Northern Ireland, and her grandfather had promised his dying daughter that he would keep her girls together and raise them—a promise he was resolved to keep.

While my mother's father was alive, there was tenderness and love. Bedtime stories and soft melodies sung over sleepy children were the gifts of this single father to his motherless babies. But six months later, a natural gas leak inside a sewer pipe suffocated him. The girls were then raised in a home with a gentle but fragile and vulnerable grandmother, ruled by a harsh and embittered grandfather. While they had no deficiency of material necessities, affection, compassion, and love were commodities absent from daily life.

My mother's mother had seven brothers, all younger than she. They lived in the house with the girls and exploited them in every imaginable manner. My mother bonded with her grandmother and defended her when the grandfather would attack her physically, which would invoke his distain and redirect his wrath toward my mother. Her years with her grandparents were harsh and bitter, but they created a resiliency within her that enabled her to not only survive but thrive. It also created within her a sensitivity to those in similar circumstances.

Consequently, while she was concerned for her daughter becoming emotionally involved with a young man so aloof, she was mindful of the life experiences that had formed this protective personality around a heart scarred with a multitude of disappointments.

On one particular evening, after the gang had gone and we were washing plates and cups and tidying the parlor, my mother asked, "What do you know about this Tommy?"

My mother could interrogate with the skill of an inquisitor. "Well, he lives on Jefferson Street, and he went to Nativity School," I said.

"You need to be careful, Doris. He seems to have a great deal of knowledge of the world, much more than is beneficial," she cautioned me.

"Oh, Mom, you just need to give him a chance," I responded a little more defensively than I expected. "Tommy is really a very kind and caring person.

"I'm not saying that you can't be friends. Just go slowly, okay?"

My mother warned in a manner that indicated she had fears of which she did not want to speak. "I will, Mom. I promise."

Mom kissed me on the top of my head, in a rare unguarded moment of affection.

After I put the last dish in the cupboard and placed the folded dish towel on the counter, I started toward my room to get ready for bed. Before I reached the doorway, I turned and said, "Goodnight, Mom. I love you."

"Good night, Doris," she responded softly. Then in a hushed tone that was almost reverential, she said, "I love you too."

SEVEN

Tommy's Family

Tommy's father, Germano Serino, returned to America in 1923. He had been born in Cold Spring, New York, where his father was working, in 1905. Germano's father, Ciriaco, was what history calls a "bird of passage"—a migrant worker who came to America to work and subsequently return to Italy. Ciriaco had come to America in 1900 and established himself with adequate employment and a place to live, then sent for his wife, Emmanuella, and their four-year-old daughter, Antonietta, who arrived the following year.

The family was residing in Cold Spring when Germano and his older brother, Carminantonio (or Tonio, as the family called him), were born. Germano was six years old when the family returned to Italy, and he grew up working on the family tobacco farm.

In 1921, Tonio came to America, and after two years sent passage to fund Germano's voyage to join him. Germano was glad to be free from the family farm—a place that he loathed with intensity. He hated the sounds and smells; its grunting, snorting animals; and its horseflies incessantly buzzing around the dung-strewn stables and stalls. On dry days the farm roads were suffocatingly dusty. When it rained the mud was ankle deep.

When he arrived in America, he roomed with his brother at the home of his aunt and uncle, Carolina Serino and Nicola Parrella, and their eight children. It was crowded and noisy, and privacy was nonexistent. Nevertheless, it was safe and warm, and Germano had obtained an opportunity for a fresh start, far from the poverty and deprivation of his home across the sea.

Tonio had procured a job on the railroad for Germano, who was a diligent worker but didn't appreciate the oppressive labor and abusive foremen. Although the wages were better than anything they could earn in Italy, the brothers were aware that Italian men were earning less than American men while performing the bulk of the hard labor. Fourteen-hour workdays weren't uncommon, and while most of the American men were making twelve to thirteen dollars each week, the Italian men were compensated with eight to nine dollars a week.

After less than a year on the railroad, Germano was given the opportunity to apprentice with a welder. He soon learned not only welding but carpentry, masonry, and plastering. With these skills he eventually opened a small contracting business, Serino Construction Company, which was fully operational by the time his son Tommy was a young man.

Once he became a journeyman welder, Germano was earning enough money to move out of his aunt and uncle's house and become a border with a family from his hometown in Italy. He appreciated his aunt and uncle but felt that they were stricter with him and his brother than with their own children. Germano was a spirited and self-sufficient young man, and by the age of twenty he was prepared to determine his own destiny.

The Bocchino family, with whom he boarded, were kind and treated him with dignity and respect. They had a daughter named Maria, whom everyone called Mariuccia or "Little Mary," and Maria had a friend named Louise Stisi, whom everyone called "Sophie." Sophie was a handsome woman with dark hair, fair skin, and light eyes. She and Germano became friends and soon began courting.

However, Sophie was a peculiar woman whose eccentricities were forged in the crucible of familial tragedy and excessive mollycoddling. At her birth, Sophie's mother contracted septicemia and died at the age of twenty-four, leaving two small children and a three-week-old infant. Her father was a tailor and couldn't care for his children and provide for them simultaneously, so he prepared to place them in an orphanage. His mother wouldn't permit him to abandon infant Sophie in the orphanage, even for a brief period until another marriage could be arranged, so she brought the baby into her care and raised the child as her daughter.

It has been said that the grandmother taught Sophie two things in life: how to cook (Sophie was rumored to be the best cook in the city), and how to manipulate others for selfish gain. She indulged Sophie, yielding to her every desire and cultivating a self-perception of entitlement and a response of wrath if her will was opposed. Sophie was by any estimation one of the most self-centered, vindictive, and miserable individuals one could know. Unfortunately, these selfish tendencies were hidden to Germano in the beginning of their relationship. He only saw the jovial, humorous qualities of her personality and her superb culinary talents and believed her to be a prime candidate for a wife and mother. They were married on April 18, 1926, and began life together with optimism, unaware of the seeds of discord that would soon develop deep roots.

Their first several years together were a mix of domestic tranquility and frequent episodes of pouting and sulking by Sophie if her peremptory requests were not acceptably addressed. Four children were born during that time: Jerry, the oldest and most favored by Sophie; Dolores; Tommy; and Emmanuella, called Emily.

Germano made great efforts to be a good father and husband. Each morning he made breakfast for the children and brought a fresh cup of coffee to Sophie's bedside. If it was during a time when she wasn't speaking to him, he simply left it on the nightstand near the bed. Once the children's needs were satisfied, he was off to work.

Upon arriving home, Sophie would usually be preparing dinner, and Germano would play with the children. The children were always excited to see their dad return home from work, but the welcome was not as warm from Sophie. Germano was never certain how he might find his wife, whether in good humor or sullen and withdrawn, and it became increasingly difficult when the children were in bed. Sophie would often go to bed first, and when Germano would reach for her, she would turn her back to him. The periods of separation and isolation became progressively longer and more frequent and would soon reach a breaking point.

In 1933, Sophie became seriously ill with pneumonia. She was hospitalized for several weeks, and during that time, ten-month-old Emily also contracted pneumonia. The child was not so fortunate, and after a brief but severe illness, she died. Germano was broken, knowing his wife was battling the same illness that had just claimed the life of his daughter, and he didn't tell Sophie of Emily's death until Sophie was well on the road to recovery. By that time, the baby was buried, and Sophie was furious.

She channeled her grief into rage, with Germano as the target. She blamed him for the child's death, accusing him of negligence and disregard for her and Emily's life. With her angry words she drove the wedge of separation between them deeper, and the unraveling of their marital unity spiraled further downward.

Sophie became an impenetrable wall, cutting off all physical contact and keeping verbal communication to a minimum. Germano soon took the separate bedroom on the opposite side of the apartment. He would still prepare breakfast for the children and bring the coffee to his silent wife and leave it on the bedstand, but things had changed. Germano once confessed that his physical needs were far beyond what a young man could endure and so he began to seek the fulfillment of those needs outside of his home. He would return home from work, bathe, dress, and then leave. There was no more interaction with the children and no more paternal affection. Their mother was completely self-absorbed, wallowing in the pitiful melancholy she alone had created. It was as the proverb says: A wise woman builds her house, but a foolish woman tears it down with her own hands. Sophie was a most foolish woman.

When there is discord in the home, and husband and wife retreat to separate lives filled with self-gratification, the children are summarily abandoned. Consequently, at the age of five, Tommy Serino was alone and confused. He was discarded by his father, who justified himself as a spurned husband with neglected needs and presumed the burden of childcare would be undertaken by the mother. But Tommy was rejected by his mother, who justified herself as an abused wife whose husband could not meet her requirements. Tommy was on his own to fend for himself, to provide for himself, and to care for himself.

The loneliness and emptiness were all-consuming. What had he done to merit this desertion? If he could just understand, maybe his daddy would come back home, and maybe his mommy would love him like she did his brother. Maybe he wouldn't be so all alone, so frightened, and maybe life wouldn't be so futile and perplexing. Each day he returned home from school to an empty house. His family had scattered to the four winds, each searching for something to fill the void. He would prepare something to eat and leave the house to walk the streets.

Christmastime was particularly difficult for Tommy. There were no presents, no family celebration, and no acknowledgment of the holiday aside from a few household decorations, a small tree, and the trays of cookies his mother baked for her friends. The year that Tommy was eight years old, he heard that a benevolent group was giving away toys for children who had no Christmas gifts at home. Although Tommy's dad was a successful contractor and could well afford to buy presents for his children, he was completely involved in his own life, separate from his family. To his children, he was a border in their home, a phantom that appeared and just as quickly vanished. So, on the specified day, Tommy walked to the Bardavon Theatre, where signs proclaimed that toys for underprivileged children could be obtained.

The building was crowded, and the atmosphere was chaotic and confused. A tall woman came to Tommy and asked if he was here for the toys and where his parents were. Tommy was embarrassed, and the kind woman sensed his discomfort. She took him to the stage, where he was permitted to fill a bag with toys from one of the several bins brimming with donations from caring benefactors.

Tommy made his selections and turned to leave, and the tall woman redirected him to stand in a line with other children in the middle of the stage while a man who appeared to be some sort of clergyman made a rambling speech in which he made frequent references to the disadvantaged children on the stage.

Tommy was mortified and deeply regretted his decision to attend the gift distribution. As he scanned the crowd, a thousand eyes were gawking at him with pity and pathos. He could feel their sympathy overflowing and suffocating him with the sickening sweetness of their good deeds. As his humiliation reached a climax, the children on the stage were dismissed. Tommy ran all the way home to his empty house, placed the toys under the meager Christmas tree, and fell on his bed and wept from shame.

As the years passed, Tommy made friends outside the home, and they filled the void left by his parents. He spent most of his time with his friends, and as young boys will, they looked for ways to fill the long evenings and weekends outside of school. Trouble was never far away. They would engage in all kinds of mischief, and their antics were relatively benign, never causing harm to others or damage to property. The boys would sneak onto the church property and steal cherries from the cherry tree at the convent. Likewise, as equal-opportunity thieves, they would saunter up to Bridge Street to the synagogue and steal the vegetables from the rabbi's garden.

As they grew older, the boys discovered alcohol. They were too young to drink but managed to procure liquor consistently. They soon became regulars at all the local taverns. There were times when an evening at the bar or a football game at the sandlot would erupt in a brawl. Tommy had developed an unfettered disputatiousness and this, along with a quick temper, often resulted in fist fights. There seemed to be no escape from the repressed anger contained deep in his soul.

As his sixteenth birthday approached, Tommy became excited at the prospect of a birthday party. Four years earlier his mother had acknowledged his brother's sixteenth birthday with a cake and a surprise party for him and a few close friends. Tommy was certain that he could expect a similar acknowledgment. When the day arrived, he looked for clues to confirm his suspicions—the aroma of a cake baking, unidentified boxes possibly concealing assorted party favors, a random package of balloons, something, anything. But everything was the same. He was confused but speculated that the party would be that night, rather than in the afternoon. After all, it was a Wednesday.

So Tommy went to school and hurried home to find his house empty as usual. He waited an inordinate amount of time for a party that never materialized. His disappointment was surpassed only by his self-reproach for being so naïve as to believe that his family deemed him worthy of such recognition. He would never believe himself worthy of anything meaningful again, and he would never have a birthday party until he was thirty-seven years old and his wife affirmed his value.

Tommy's dysfunctional family and the abandonment he endured in his childhood resulted in deep scars and heartbreaking memories that would torment him for the rest of his life. His childhood experiences influenced his selfperception, and the trauma of neglect affected his ability to form and sustain relationships, as well as his capacity to love and receive love in return. His sense of self-worth and personal value were damaged beyond hope. As the sins of the parents were visited on Tommy, he became a young man crying out to be known, loved, and valued.

EIGHT

Winter of 1948

I t was late autumn 1948 and the school year was well underway. We were already halfway through the first term. Unfortunately, things were not going well for me. I had spoken to my parents about my frustrations with obtaining the proper classes and they had advised me to try to register for the appropriate subjects again this year, but that hadn't happened.

I wasn't able to enroll in the classes necessary to complete the secretarial program, and the only classes my guidance counselor could offer me encompassed a broad range of study. Following this curriculum, I wouldn't acquire a diploma in secretarial studies and would instead graduate with a general degree, which was basically useless. I was beyond frustrated and determined that if I couldn't successfully attain the required classes for the second term, I would quit school.

After a few months of me dating Sam Ciofi and Tommy dating Eleanor DiPilco, he and I were together again. With the holidays approaching, one morning I asked

Tommy about his family. He had always been mysterious about his home life, which piqued my curiosity, so I attempted to approach the subject delicately by asking a simple question about Thanksgiving.

We were just past Market Street and most of the gang was ahead of us. Tommy had been talking about an odd job he was doing with his Uncle Mike at Vassar Hospital, when I rather abruptly asked him, "Tommy, what's your family doing for Thanksgiving?"

He looked at me as if I'd just asked him what the meaning of life was—an odd blank stare, as if the inquiry was completely incomprehensible.

So I rephrased the question and posed it in a less direct manner. "I mean, are you guys having a turkey for Thanksgiving?" I then realized this was a stupid question since, after all, every family in America eats turkey on Thanksgiving.

Tommy seemed to revive. "Nope."

I didn't really understand his answer, so I questioned him again. "Well, are you going to visit relatives for—"

"We're not doing anything for Thanksgiving," he interrupted me. "We don't ever do anything."

I fell silent. What could he mean by this?

Evidently, Tommy realized that a little more information would be necessary to help me grasp the concept. "My family doesn't do anything together. We're not a normal family." Then Tommy said nothing more. With his face a fusion of pain, anger, and sorrow, he appeared as though he had the weight of the world on his shoulders.

I didn't know how to respond. I couldn't understand what an abnormal family could be, or what the dynamics were in Tommy's home. I didn't know what to say to make him feel less burdened, but I desperately wanted to relieve the apparent misery I had brought upon him. "Well, you can come to our house if you like. We always cook a turkey for Thanksgiving."

Tommy's countenance softened slightly, and he smiled a half-smile at me. "No, thanks," he said quietly. "I'll be fine. It's just another day."

A thought occurred to me then—a somewhat crazy notion at this moment, for certain. I summoned the courage necessary, took a deep breath, and said, "I'd like to meet your family sometime."

He huffed. "Oh, you would, would you?"

"Yes, I would," I said defiantly. "Since we're going together, it only seems right that I should get to know your family, right?"

Tommy snickered. "There's time for that. You'll meet them soon enough." And the conversation ended just as we arrived at school.

It was now late November, and Poughkeepsie was alive with Christmas spirit. The city had strung Christmas lights across every block on Main Street all the way from the river to Arlington. Store windows were festively adorned with competing holiday displays, some of which were animated with mechanical figurines.

My favorite display was the enormous columns of lights that formed the image of a Christmas tree on either side of the Lucky Platt building. The lights stretched from the top floor of the building to the ground level, covering the façade on the Main Street and the Academy Street sides. There were large Christmas trees at numerous points in the city, Eastman Park, College Hill, and scattered from east to west across town. The local stores that normally closed promptly at five in the evening were now open until nine, and shoppers took full advantage of the extended hours to acquire their Yuletide treasures.

The larger department stores—Wallace's, Grant's, and Lucky Platt's—led the charge in the holiday frenzy, offering sales, discounts, and layaway plans to entice bargain hunters in the spirit of Christmastime commercialism. People bustled up and down Main Street carrying shopping bags full of gifts, some of which were already wrapped as a complimentary service of the season. Everyone seemed in a hurry, yet there was always time for a sidewalk chat with friends and neighbors. Holiday greetings and well wishes were exchanged, invitations were extended and accepted, and a convivial attitude prevailed upon all.

Churches were equally involved in the spirit of the nativity. Catholic churches displayed ornate manger scenes outside their chapels, rectories, and convents. Protestant churches preferred greenery and were adorned with holly, wreaths, and garlands. The synagogue on Bridge Street was not exempt from the holiday spirit, with a large menorah on exhibit in a place of prominence. On each night of Chanukah an additional light was illuminated, until the menorah was in full radiance.

As Christmas drew closer, thoughts of holiday dinners brought customers to local food markets, bakeries, and pastry shops. The Mohican Market was the largest of these and boasted an abundance of essentials for homemade holiday treats: figs, currants, and raisins; flour, sugar, and lard; and everything else necessary to create a confectionery paradise. There were also live geese, chickens, and turkeys available as the centerpiece of Christmas dinner. Fresh fruits were rare, but citrus was occasionally trucked in from Florida.

The smaller neighborhood grocers and bakeries were lively with customers looking for special treats. Ethnic pastry shops featured a touch of nostalgia for immigrants and their children. German shops offered stollens, strudels, and gingerbreads, while Italian shops advertised panettone, cassata, torrone, and of course Perugia chocolate. Gadelleto's Fish Market was preparing for the Christmas Eve extravaganza, as scores of families would gather outside the building early in the morning to buy the freshest fish for the vigil of Christmas. For the entire day, the small market would be overwhelmed with customers searching for the best quality pulpi, calamari, scungili, and baccala.

Holidays were always a big celebration at my house, but Christmas was the biggest of them all. My mother absolutely loved Christmas and gave the full measure of her effort to make it a glorious success. The house was completely decorated with everything from a nativity scene to a large Christmas tree adorned with lights, ornaments, and tinsel in the center of the parlor. She would bake hundreds of cookies as well as cakes, pies, and breads. When I was young, the holidays were alternated: one year with her family and the next year with Daddy's family. But since we moved to Poughkeepsie, Christmas was always at our house and the family from both sides would gather around our table. My mother's sister, Betty, and her husband, Okey, would attend, and my dad's brothers would come from Newburgh with their families. My sister's current boyfriend would also appear at some point in the day since Kay wasn't allowed to go out on Christmas. The house would be full and alive with laughter and playful banter.

Food was available all day long, and at some point the men would set up a table and play cards while they drank their wine and smoked their pungent cigars. That is, until my mother came into the room and chased them out onto the porch to indulge.

Few presents were exchanged. Gifts were primarily for the children, although occasionally someone would bring a household gift such as a set of doilies; a basket of home-made bread, sausage, and wine; or a knitted item; but generally the Christmas gift we all enjoyed was each other.

This year I had invited Tommy to come over, even for just a short time, but he declined, saying he didn't want to intrude on our family celebration. So I was pleasantly surprised when Tommy arrived late in the afternoon with a present for me.

"Tommy, I'm so glad you came," I squealed in delight when I opened the door in response to his knock. "Please come in."

"No, no. I don't want to impose on your family," he protested.

Suddenly, my Aunt Eleanor came to the door. "Who is this handsome devil?" she exclaimed, then grabbed Tommy by the hand and tried to tug him inside.

Tommy recoiled, but Aunt Eleanor was undeterred. "Come on, son. I don't bite!" He couldn't resist her ostenta-tious manner and relented, entering the house. He was uncomfortable as a horse in a glue factory, with the jovial mood and crowd of relatives all staring at him, making their initial judgments.

I took him by the hand and led him over to my dad and uncles. "Tommy, you know my dad," I said.

"Hello, Mr. Messina. Merry Christmas," Tommy said prudently.

"Merry Christmas, son," my dad said. "You want a glass of wine?"

"No, thank you, sir," Tommy politely responded.

I jumped in to continue the introductions. "This is my uncle Carm, my uncle Pete, and my uncle Angelo. And over there asleep on the couch is my uncle Okey," I said with a giggle at the sight of bald-headed Uncle Okey with his head back and mouth open, snoring a Yuletide chorus.

"So you're Doris's boy, huh?" Uncle Carm asked.

"Yes, and he's a good fellow, Uncle Carm," I chimed in.

"Well, he better be," my uncle warned.

My mother came to the rescue from the kitchen. "Can I get you something to eat, Tommy?" she asked, giving the bad eye to Uncle Carm.

"No, thank you, Mrs. Messina. I can't stay."

Mom smiled. "Of course. You probably have family obligations today." I could tell she was probing.

"Not really. I'm just meeting my friends at the corner," Tommy replied honestly.

She looked sad momentarily. "Then you must take something with you," she said and darted for the kitchen before Tommy could protest.

I took Tommy away from the gaggle of relatives to the front porch, where he said, "I brought something for you, Doris. It's not much, but I wanted to get you a present for Christmas."

Surprised, I blushed.

Tommy handed me a small box wrapped neatly in foil Christmas paper with Santa Claus heads surrounded by holly. I tore the paper and opened the box to reveal a small gold bracelet. "You can wear it on your wrist or your ankle, whichever you prefer," Tommy said. "I hope you like it."

I was overwhelmed. "It's beautiful, Tommy, too nice to

wear on my ankle. Would you help me put it on my wrist, please?"

Without a word, Tommy took the bracelet and fixed it securely on my wrist. I was so excited that without thinking I gave him a big hug. "Thank you, Tommy. I love it."

Now it was his turn to blush. "Well, I've got to go now. I'll see you sometime this week," Tommy said, and with that he was gone.

I opened the door and stepped back into the house, oblivious to the cacophony of noise around me. I was caught up in the moment, so much so that I didn't hear my mother speaking to me at first.

"Doris, I asked you where Tommy is," she said, approaching me. "I've got a plate for him."

"Oh. Uh, he had to leave. He probably just forgot."

She shook her head and turned back toward the kitchen. "That's a strange one, he is, that boy."

Aunt Ella was the first to notice the bracelet. "What is this?" she asked in a volume intended to draw everyone's attention. Her eyes twinkled. "A gold bracelet, huh? Somebody got hit with the thunderbolt."

"Thunderbolt, my *culo*," Uncle Carm said. "Who gives a gold bracelet to my little girl?"

Uncle Pete offered an explanation to everyone's concerns. "You know, sweetie, a gift of gold means the boy's intentions are serious. He's an Italian boy, so he knows what he's doing."

"Well, I like him," Aunt Ella said after a few moments of silence in the room.

"You just wish you were twenty years younger," Uncle Carm teased.

"*Vafungulo*," she responded, and the mood was instantly lighter.

Later that night, when the tables were cleared, the floors were swept, the relatives had all gone home for the night, and another Christmas holiday was successfully completed, Mom and I finished putting the dishes away in the kitchen. "Why do you think he didn't stay, Mom?" I asked.

She turned toward me, wiping her hands on a dishtowel. "I can't be sure, honey. Maybe he just isn't comfortable around a lot of people."

That didn't really answer my question. "But why would he go out and meet his friends on the corner? Didn't he have any family at his house?"

"Well, honey, not everyone has a family like you have," she explained.

"But he could have stayed with our family. It seemed like he wanted to but he was, I don't know, afraid or something," I said, still trying to understand.

Sadness tinged my mother's expression. "When someone doesn't have a close family, they don't know how to act around a close family. It makes them uncomfortable."

I went to bed that night trying to understand it all—Tommy's leaving and my mother's explanation. What was so different between my family and Tommy's family?

Then I looked at the bracelet gracing my wrist and realized that whatever the difference between our families, Tommy still cared for me.

NINE
My Family

My parents had a solid marriage, one that developed its enduring power as a result of circumstances that would've devastated persons of irresolute character. They persevered through the Great Depression and the war, as many couples in that era, but it was their unique trials and tragedies that drew them together in an inseparable bond of unity. The first time my mother saw my father was on the worst day of his life.

My dad was the oldest of seven children born to Santo Messina and Catina Profeta, both from Villa Rosa in the province of Enna in central Sicily. My grandfather was a large man with a dark complexion, a quick temper, and little tolerance for anything contrary to his own desires. He began his career in New York City's Little Italy on the Lower East Side as a laborer, but eventually purchased a pushcart from which he sold lemon ice. He found more success when he began to sell "washing fluid," a combination of detergent and bleach used by housewives for cleaning clothes.

Santo was an unscrupulous man, not above bending the rules to make personal gains. It's rumored that during Prohibition the jugs he delivered to his customers held more than just washing fluid. Whatever he may have been selling, Santo made enough money to purchase some property in New Windsor, New York, and escape the slums of the city for a better opportunity for his children.

The property was at the corner of Walsh Road and Meriline Avenue and featured two houses. The smaller house had a tavern on the bottom floor and two apartments above. The large house was at the center of the property and had an abundance of room for the growing Messina family. They lived in that house for fifteen years and had seven children: Giuseppe (my father), Serafina, Pietro, Providenza, Carmine, Angelo, and Santo. Also living in the house were my father's grandmother, Providenza Alu, and two other women: a mother known as "Cumma" Jenny Crisci and her daughter, Victoria.

My grandmother was a soft-spoken woman with a kind and gentle manner. She was devoted to her children, but her primary love was "her Giuseppe," my father. She always wore an apron over her dress, and in the pocket of that apron was a small, black change purse that contained two things: a set of rosary beads and my father's photograph.

My grandfather was domineering and ruled his home like a tyrant. He was abusive toward my grandmother and not above physical violence to ensure that his will was law. This continued until my father was in his late teens. My daddy adored his mother and didn't appreciate the treatment she received from his father.

One day, when my grandfather was mistreating my grandmother, my father ran into the room. After shoving his father and striking him, he warned, "Don't you ever lay a hand on my mother again or I will kill you."

Santo was furious that his domination had been challenged, and he threatened my father vehemently, but he never struck my grandmother again. My dad didn't respect his father and regarded him as a cruel and vile man unworthy of such esteem. Contrarily, he adored his mother and would do anything to protect her and demonstrate his love for her.

The women in the Messina household were not permitted to seek employment outside of the home. Consequently, they would gather on several evenings each week and sew coats from the factory up the street. One of the young boys, Carmine or Angelo, would go to the factory with a wagon and pick up a load of coats and bring them to the house. The women, including my grandmother and her mother, Cumma Jenny and Victoria, and my father's oldest sister, Serafina, also called Fanny, would gather in my grandmother's kitchen and sew buttonholes, stitch linings, add collars, or perform countless other small sewing tasks on the garments. They were paid several cents for each finished piece that was returned to the factory. It was a cheerful, social time as the women would stitch and baste and converse, sharing anecdotes and opinions.

Early in 1928, the Messinas took in a border, a young man from their *paese* in Sicily who was down on his luck and needing a fresh start. The young man, Pasquale "Patsy" Parino, was a melancholic personality who remained aloof and much preferred the solitude of his room to any collective interaction with the family. He was brusque with the adult members of the Messina clan, expressing only modest respect for Catina and Santo. He despised my father and tolerated the children, but he absolutely hated Cumma Jenny and Victoria. No one understood why he had such strong feelings of animosity toward them, and they were careful to stay out of his way whenever he was around.

Santo was good to the young man despite his strange behaviors and lack of appreciation. He secured a job for Patsy as a laborer; gave him his own large room off the kitchen, apart from the rest of the family in consideration of his privacy; and permitted him to come and go as he pleased. Catina would encourage him to participate in family meals, but he always politely declined, favoring the isolation of his private quarters. The only person in the family he genuinely cared for was the grandmother, whom he referred to as "Ma."

Aside from the Messinas, Patsy had little interaction with others in the neighborhood apart from Mr. Cordelli, the owner of the small grocery store on the opposite side of the street. This was unusual since there was a large number of Sicilians in the community. Many of the neighborhood men would gather at the tavern operated by Louie Thompson, a Sicilian man with an anglicized name, where they would play cards or "fingers" and drink wine. Patsy never entered the establishment and had a great disdain for Louie.

As time passed, Patsy became more distant and withdrawn from the family. He confided in Cordelli that he had a growing contempt for Santo and his success in business. "I don't understand why everything comes so easy for him, when life is so hard for me," he complained to the grocer. "Everything he touches turns into gold."

Cordelli cautioned him not to become envious of another man's achievements. "It will bring the *malocchio*," he warned.

By October of 1929, Patsy had become so consumed with envy of Santo that he could not tolerate his presence. He had attempted to find alternative housing, but because of his reputation as a loner, no other Sicilian families were willing to take him as a boarder. Even Cordelli balked, insisting that he had no room for another resident.

The night of October twelfth my father was to attend a party. After dinner he washed, dressed, and prepared to go out, then approached his mother in the kitchen and kissed her. "I really don't feel like going to this party tonight, Ma," he said. "Maybe I'll just stay home."

"Oh, no, no, Giuseppe. You go," his mother protested. "There's no reason for you to stay here tonight. The ladies are coming over to sew coats later, and you know what *chiachiarone* we become. You would have no peace. Go and have a good time. I love you, my sweet son."

"I love you too, Ma." He left the house, and at starting down the street, he noticed that Cordelli's grocery store was dark. *How strange that Cordelli would close so early on a Friday night*, he thought.

As the women began to gather, Catina brought the coats from the spare room and laid them on the kitchen table, already cleared and cleaned from the evening meal. Santo was about to leave for a Friday night card game at Louie Thompson's tavern, and as he reached the kitchen doorway, Cumma Jenny and Victoria were coming toward it. Cumma Jenny was a tall, very obese woman whose dark hair was always pulled securely back into a tight bun. She and Santo reached the door at the same time, and it proved impossible for both to pass through together. Santo glared at Cumma Jenny, and she timidly backed up to allow him passage, then entered the kitchen.

Victoria pulled the chairs around in a circle, ensuring

that the large oak rocking chair was reserved for the grand-mother. As the women selected the garment they would labor on that evening, Fanny arrived and dutifully took her place. Although she was eighteen years old, she was not permitted social interaction with young men since her father was arranging a marriage for her. Fanny had long ago resigned herself to the station assigned to her in life, and her resilient spirit compelled her to accomplish all that was possible within those parameters.

The grandmother came into the kitchen, and before taking her seat in the rocking chair, she approached the table to search for the coat she had been working on earlier in the week. It was the season for men's overcoats, and the long, gray woolen jacket had been problematic for her to manipulate as she sewed the lining inside. She was deter-mined to conquer the task this evening. She would not permit any piece of clothing to have the victory over her. Soon the ladies were chatting and sewing and enjoying each other's company.

As Cumma Jenny was telling a story about the man who sold a blind goat to her father, a story they'd heard numerous times before, footsteps came up the stairs. The women fell silent when Patsy entered the room. He looked angry and didn't even acknowledge the ladies when they greeted him cordially. He just went to his room and closed the door.

They whispered about how Patsy had been very sullen and irritable of late and any communication from him was generally mean and surly. When Catina said that she felt sorry for him, Cumma Jenny warned that Santo should put him out, and soon.

Moments later Patsy burst from his room with a sawed-off shotgun, took aim at the circle of ladies, and fired. Catina's chair was facing away from him, and she received the first blast directly in the upper torso. She was completely unaware of what had happened. She heard an explosion, felt a searing pain in her back and was dead before her body struck the floor. Shocked, the other women froze. The grandmother could only stare at the body of her daughter lying on the floor in an ever-increasing pool of blood.

"I'm not going to kill you, Ma," Patsy told her. "You have to take care of the children." His plan was to kill all the older members of the Messina family: Santo, Catina, Giuseppe, and Fanny.

The other women tried to scatter. Patsy shot Victoria in the chest before she could rise, and the force of the blast knocked her over the back of the chair and into the wall. He then shot Cumma Jenny in the back as she rushed toward the doorway. Fanny had run in the opposite direction, hurried up the stairs, and opened the window to flee down the fire escape. Patsy followed her, came out onto the fire escape, and took aim. As she turned to see if he was pursuing her, he fired. The discharge was weakened by the distance Fanny had managed to put between them, but several pieces of buckshot tore through her face.

With Patsy gone, the grandmother left the house and ran down the street to Louie Thompson's tavern where Santo was playing cards. She burst into the room, crying and screaming, "Santo, come quickly. Patsy has gone crazy. He's shooting up your family."

Santo tore out the door, crossed the street, and rounded the corner to enter the front of his house. Patsy was still on the fire escape and braced the shotgun against the iron railing, anticipating Santo's movements. He lay waiting for Santo to come into view, and as Santo came around the corner and passed under the lamppost, Patsy pulled the trigger, unloading both barrels of the shotgun into the approaching man.

On the opposite side of the street, a young girl, Alice Ogle, was visiting a friend. When the gunfire began, the friend's mother entered the living room in a panic, commanded the girls to get down on the floor, and pulled the shades down. Curious, Alice crept over to the window and peeked out at the moment Santo Messina ran under the streetlamp. She would never forget the sight of Santo being shot and falling to the ground.

After killing Santo, Patsy returned to his room to wait for Giuseppe.

But before Giuseppe returned home, a mob of Santo's friends from the neighborhood stormed into the house to seize Patsy. One of the neighbors called the police, but they refused to come—after all, it was "only dagos shooting each other." The neighborhood men stormed up the stairs, led by Louie Thompson, whose intention it was "to tear Patsy apart with his bare hands." When Patsy heard the men coming, he placed the butt of the gun against the footboard of the bed and took off his shoes, then placed his big toe on the trigger. As the men burst into his room, Patsy pulled the trigger and unloaded both barrels of the shotgun into his stomach.

Catina was pronounced dead at the scene. The others were taken to St. Luke's Hospital. Santo was dead on arrival, while Victoria was hospitalized in critical condition. She was not expected to live, but miraculously recovered. Cumma Jenny had been shot in the side, but because she had turned and ran, and in no small part due to her obesity, no vital organs were affected. She was hospitalized but recovered quickly. Fanny received wounds to the face and head and was left with minor scarring that she carried with her for the remaining eighty years of her life.

Patsy also lived, and when he awoke in the hospital with his abdomen stitched, he realized that his life was now marked, for certainly one of Santo's many friends or the oldest son, Giuseppe, would hunt him down and kill him. So Patsy tore open the stitches and bled to death in the hospital room.

Giuseppe, my father, was at the party when several neighbors came to inform him of the tragedy taking place at his house. It wasn't until he arrived home that he learned of his mother's death. The street outside of the Messina property was filled with neighbors, among them my mother, Alice Ogle, and her friend. When my father realized that his beloved mother was gone, her life taken in a cruel act by a crazed psychopath, he collapsed under the burden of grief.

That was the first time my mother saw my father.

TEN

A Rough Start

I n the weeks following the death of his parents, my father, Giuseppe, went out almost every night and began to drink heavily. Since he didn't shirk his responsibilities at home, his grandmother said nothing about his behavior, secretly hoping that he would abandon these destructive activities before they could arrange a marriage for him.

His father, Santo, had previously attempted to arrange a match with a girl named Rosa from Rochester, New York. She was the daughter of a business associate, and the match was potentially lucrative for Santo, but my father refused to meet the girl or her family, saying, "I'll marry who I want, when I want!" This infuriated Santo because his son's rebellious attitude had humiliated him in front of people he desired to impress. Now that Santo was dead, the responsibility for arrangement of marriages fell to the grandmother, but she would tread lightly while my father was in this fragile state.

One evening, my dad met a girl at a dance on Mount

Beacon and asked to walk her home. The girl was Anna Ogle, my mother's younger sister. When they arrived at the house on Water Street that she shared with her grandmother and sisters, my mother, Alice, was sitting on the front porch. She recognized my father and was taken by his dark Mediterranean features and charismatic personality. Alice and my father conversed for a long time, and he asked if he could see her again. Over the next few months, they saw each other frequently and in a short time became a couple. Then, at the beginning of the summer of 1930, my mother told my father that she was pregnant.

When my father told his grandmother about the situation, she was devastated. "What's the matter with you, Giuseppe? Why are you spending time with this Medigan *puttana lorda?*" she exclaimed, sobbing. "It's not your fault. She put a curse on you. We can send you to Sicily. You can stay with my brother."

"No, Ma. Listen," my father said. "I love Alice. I want to marry her. I could never leave her, especially now."

"She has bewitched you, Giuseppe! Please don't do this. What would your mother say?"

At the mention of his mother, my dad grew angry. "My mother would love her and would be happy for me." He stormed out of the house and didn't return until late that night.

My mother shared the news with her family, and the response was quite the same. Her oldest sister, Betty, ranted, "Why do you even associate with these guineas? They're no good, the whole lot of them."

My mother ignored her sister and appealed to her grandmother, "Ma, you met Joe. You know that he's a good fellow."

Her grandmother remained quiet, seemingly lost in her

thoughts. Finally, she said with her Irish brogue, "Where will you live? We have no room here for another family." She was, as always, practical and pragmatic.

"Well, Ma, the Messinas own that property with a couple of houses. I'm certain we could sort something out there," my mother said.

"You mean the house where the parents were murdered? And what kind of violence are you subjecting yourself to there, my darling? I've heard that these people are ruthless and aggressive, that brutality is a way of life and bloodshed is common among them. This family has already proven this to be true. What of your safety, my love?"

"Ma, you know that Joe isn't like that," my mother gently protested to her grandmother. "Neither is his family. What happened to them could have happened to anyone. Please, Ma, I love him and I'm going to have his baby, your great-grandchild."

The grandmother was not convinced but was overwhelmed with love for my mother. "Oh, my sweetheart, you know I only want the best for you. Why don't you bring Joe over next week for dinner and we'll get to know him some."

My mother threw her arms around her grandmother. "I will, Ma. Thank you. I love you."

"I love you too, my darling," she responded tearfully.

My parents were married the next month, in the home of the Presbyterian minister, with Vincent and Teresa DiChiaro, my father's best friend and his wife as witnesses. They then rented the front apartment of the small building on the Messina property, and it was there that Kay was born.

Kay's birth was extremely difficult for my mother. She was exhausted from days of labor, and when the baby was born the household scale recorded her weight as fourteen pounds. Whether this is completely accurate or not is unknown. But she did weigh over ten pounds at birth according to the doctor at his first visit. My mother had lost a great deal of blood, and her weight had dropped to below ninety pounds. Her condition was critical and she should have gone to the hospital but instead chose to remain at home. The care she received from my father's grandmother, as well as Cumma Jenny and Victoria, proved far superior to any offered by the finest medical facilities.

The new baby brought little change to the attitude and behavior of Joe's grandmother. While she was thrilled to be a great-grandmother and doted on the baby, she was critical of my mother. Many nights she would bring food over for my father saying, "These Medigan women don't know how to cook. You'll starve if you try to eat the *merde* that she puts on your table."

She was constantly interfering, coming to the house anytime she wanted and taking Kay back to her house, where she would keep her for hours. When my mother would go to retrieve Kay, my father's grandmother would complain to him that his wife wouldn't let her see the baby.

My father continued to go out to the tavern each night and would often come home drunk. One evening he came home late and began vomiting on the front stoop. While my mother was chastising him, reminding him that he was not a single man any longer and that he had a family that depended on him, his grandmother was rubbing his back and telling him, "Don't listen to her, Giuseppe. She's no good anyway." Then she turned to my mother and said, "What's the matter with you? He's a young man. He has a right to go out. Do you want him *fa'un culo tou simpre?*"

Since my mother didn't understand Sicilian, my aunt

Prov translated for her. This scenario continued for the first three years of their marriage, and had my mother not been a feisty woman who learned to fight for what was hers, the grandmother would have broken up the family.

My mother became pregnant again soon after Kay was born, but her body wasn't healthy enough to carry another child yet. My brother, Joseph, was stillborn at seven months gestation. Almost immediately my mother was pregnant again, this time with me. This time my father was very concerned for his wife and the baby. He became a more responsible husband, putting aside the juvenile behaviors he had embraced. He was home each night for dinner and remained home to care for his expectant wife, determined to do his part to ensure this baby would be born healthy.

He also began to defend his wife against the criticism of his grandmother. One evening she came to the house as my mother was serving dinner. My mother had made baked beans and scalloped potatoes, and when she saw it, the grandmother said, "What is that *merde?* No one could eat that."

"Taste it before you comment," my father insisted.

When she did, a look of surprise and delight came over her face. She sat down, took a plate, and served herself a large portion of the baked beans and potatoes that had now become her new favorite food.

As the years passed, my father's grandmother came to accept my mother and then to truly love her. My mother was good to the grandmother but took a firm stance against her interference. The grandmother respected the boundaries my mother set and enjoyed having her two great-granddaughters living in the house across the yard. When she would see us outside, she would shout from the front stoop or the kitchen window, *"Che bedda sta fighia!"* and squeal with delight as we scampered across the grass for treats.

My mother never denied her access to Kay and me, and truly appreciated having her help with Kay while she was caring for me when I was an infant. The younger Messina boys were getting older and spent more time outside the home, so their grandmother would come over to visit with my mother most evenings. She would talk about her daughter, her family in Sicily, and other subjects that were important to her.

At first it was difficult because my mother spoke no Sicilian and the grandmother spoke no English, but after some time my mother started to learn Sicilian. The grandmother was thrilled to have another woman to converse with, in her own language, beside the Criscis, with whom she was frequently at odds. She was also happy that Giuseppe's wife was trying to speak her language, even if she was hard to understand at times.

Many years of hard labor began taking their toll on the grandmother, and her feet became so painful from arthritis that walking became difficult. Soon she was unable to make the short walk across the yard to visit, so my mother would go to the grandmother's house and massage her feet and legs, applying lotion and rubbing the weariness of life from them. A thousand acts of kindness and care from my mother wore down the grandmother's fear, disappointment, and anger that had marred the initial years of their relationship, and it sowed the seeds of mutual respect and genuine love between them.

When the grandmother passed away suddenly in 1937, my mother felt the void as keenly as any of the Messinas. She would truly miss this protective woman, guardian of the family, who lived her entire life for her loved ones and who opened her heart to a stranger who became a daughter to her.

I was born on June 26, 1933, in the small house on the Messina property on the corner of Walsh Road and Merline Avenue. The big house in the middle of the field where my grandparents had lived was still standing at the time. Several years later it would burn to the ground, the result of an electrical fire. Some say the curse that claimed the lives of my grandparents also claimed the house where they died.

When I was born, the doctor was present as well as Victoria Crisci, the midwife. The birth was difficult, and neither the doctor nor the midwife could stimulate me to breathe. Finally, the doctor held my little body above the bed and dropped me, hoping that striking the bed would startle a gulp of air into my lungs. She did this three times, and on the third attempt I gasped and began to cry. The doctor gave me to my mother who immediately began to nurse me.

My father's younger brothers and their friends were all excited over the birth and were patiently waiting downstairs. As soon as they heard me crying, they came running up the stairs and were just about to burst into the room when Victoria intercepted them, saying, "You can't come in here yet. Wait until I come out for you." She gathered all the dirty and bloody cloths and hid them under the bed to be retrieved later so the boys would not see them, then allowed the boys to enter.

By that time my mother had laid me in the crib, so the boys surrounded me, pushing and shoving each other to get a better look. My uncle Carm, who was fourteen at the time, took one look at me and fell deeply in love. I was his favorite from that day forward.

We lived in the house on Walsh Road until I was five years old. Life was good for me as a little girl. We lived in the front apartment, and Aunt Prov and Uncle Morgan lived in the rear. Downstairs was empty at that time, but it had once been a saloon. An old piano remained there as a testimony to its former glory. It was completely out of tune, but occasionally my uncle Pete would come over and play the piano for us while we sang. He would always play his favorite song, "Melancholy Baby," so I knew all the words at a very young age.

Kay and I would often go into the old saloon to play. I would pretend to play the piano, imitating Uncle Pete's movements on the keys, and Kay would dance on top of the piano. It was great fun pretending to perform for a large appreciative audience that gushed with admiration for our talents.

Our home was comfortable and warm, but it had no indoor bathroom. There was an outhouse about one hundred feet from the house. This was a particular inconvenience in the winter when the outhouse was freezing cold and blocked with snow, and at nighttime when darkness obscured the way. The problem was solved by placing a chamber pot under the bed, but the disadvantage was that the chamber pot required emptying every morning. So, in the morning before we left for school, Kay and I had the duty of emptying both chamber pots—ours and our parents'—in the outhouse.

I was a small child during the Great Depression, and the gravity of such times often allude a young mind. I was truly unaware of how difficult it was for my parents to provide even basic needs. I can recall having nothing to eat at night but two small, boiled potatoes each or a bowl of macaroni with oil.

One afternoon my mother whisked our last six eggs and left them in a bowl on the counter while she picked some herbs to season them. This was all that we had for dinner that night. I was a curious four-year-old and wanted to see what was in the container that had made such a strange noise, so I reached for the bowl near the edge of the counter and spilled its entire contents on the floor. I recall my mother coming back into the house and seeing what had happened, then bursting into tears and proceeding to scrape as much of the egg back into the bowl as possible.

Many nights my parents went to bed hungry so Kay and I would have something to eat. I always marveled at the way my mother would peel potatoes. She used a paring knife, never a peeler, and would take off the thinnest layer of skin imaginable. She developed this skill during the Depression when there was little food and it was important to save as much of the potato as possible. She retained this ability for the rest of her life.

My father was often unemployed during this time since jobs were difficult to find, and when President Roosevelt's "New Deal" established the WPA, or Works Project Administration, there was hope for millions of families in similar circumstances to ours. The WPA employed mostly unskilled men to carry out public works infrastructure projects. They labored on roads, storm drains, and sewer lines, as well as built bridges, school buildings, and hospitals. The unemployment rate in 1935 was at a staggering 20 percent, and the WPA was designed to provide relief for the unemployed by providing jobs and income for millions of Americans, among them my father.

Daddy was able to procure employment at West Point digging ditches for new water lines. It was hard labor, but it provided the income necessary to sustain our family for a short time. When the work project was completed, my father was able to find work in Poughkeepsie, but this meant that we needed to relocate. I was five when we moved from New Windsor to Poughkeepsie, where we lived in the downstairs apartment at 149 Union Street.

This venture would prove to be short-lived. My mother became so homesick for New Windsor and all that was familiar that she insisted on moving back. So, after less than a year we moved back to the house on Walsh Road, now owned by Uncle Pete. Many things were so similar that it was as if we had never left, but some things had changed, and other changes were coming.

Uncle Carm married Aunt Eleanor and they would have their first son, Carmine, in 1941. Aunt Prov still lived in the rear apartment but would become a single mom of two small children during the time we lived there. A pocketbook factory would open in the building where the old coat factory once was. Uncle Carm was employed there, as well as Aunt Prov for a short time. Cordelli's grocery store was still open across the street, but my father never allowed us near the place. He had discovered that Cordelli knew of Patsy's plan to kill Santo and his family that night, but instead of warning him, out of fear he kept silent and closed his store early. His family sat in the darkness of their apartment as the tragedy unfolded. My father hated him for the rest of his life.

The Great Depression began loosening its death grip on the American people, and slowly jobs became available. But with fascism on the rise in Europe, a new threat was looming.

I was now seven years old and living in a rural area where there was no public transportation to school. Kay and I attended grade school in Cornwall, about four miles away. Each morning we would meet a group of children and make the long walk on the side of a country road, no matter what the weather. It was particularly perilous during the winter months as darkness fell and snow forced us to contend with trucks and farm vehicles on ever-narrowing roads.

While our walk to school was difficult, it paled in comparison to the trek my father made to work each day. Although we had moved back to New Windsor, my father kept his job at Goldcrest Fashions in Poughkeepsie. The job market was still unfavorable, and he had steady work with an adequate salary, so he would make the commute each day. But the trip was long and arduous and complicated by cold and heat, rain and snow.

My father would rise at five in the morning and walk from our house in New Windsor to Water Street in Newburgh. From there he would take the ferry across the river to Beacon, where he would take the train to Pough-keepsie. After disembarking the train, he would walk halfway across the city from the train station to Cherry Street in Arlington. The entire trip was twenty miles one way with approximately five miles of walking. He'd arrive back home around eight o'clock at night.

My father never wore a hat, so on rainy nights he would come in soaked through to the skin with water dripping from his hair. In winter his hair would be covered with ice, and his face, hands, and feet would be half frozen. My father battled the heat, the cold, and the elements for a year and a half before declaring to my mother, "That's it! I can't keep this up. We're moving back to Poughkeepsie." In 1941, just before the war began, we returned to lower Union Street, near South Clover Street. I've lived in Poughkeepsie ever since then.

There were definite advantages to living in Poughkeepsie. The walk to Christopher Columbus School was much shorter and less hazardous than the hike to Cornwall School. It was also nice to have my father home in the evenings. My mother did acclimate to life in Poughkeepsie, and it became easier for her when her sister moved from Newburgh to an apartment across the street from us. As time passed, my parents made many lifelong friends: Lena and Bill, Evelyn and Eddie, Mr. and Mrs. McCoy, and of course Hattie and Albert.

My family spent a lot of time with Hattie and Albert. One weekend in December, we were at their house for Sunday dinner. Just as we sat down to eat, a news bulletin interrupted the radio program that was providing background noise. "President Roosevelt has declared war on Japan," the announcer said.

Everyone rushed from the table and took a seat around the radio, and we listened as the president explained that the Japanese had bombed Pearl Harbor in an unprovoked attack and the United States was now at war. While this did come as a shock, it wasn't a complete surprise. There had been rumors of war with both Germany and Japan for some time, and it was no secret that both Europe and Asia were in the grips of conflict. Many people we knew had family in Italy who were already feeling the effects of war, and we had been subjected to blackouts and air raid drills for some time.

While at Cornwall School, we would descend a long wooden staircase to the sub-basement and sit in the dark until the air raid sirens signaled the end of the drill. I hated that basement. It was dark and damp and just plain creepy! Every home was equipped with blackout shades or curtains. When the sirens sounded, all lights went off and shades were pulled. We then sat in the dark until the siren sounded the all-clear.

To guarantee compliance, air raid wardens would walk the streets examining each house to ensure that no light could be seen. If someone even lit a cigarette, the warden would call out on his megaphone to "extinguish the light." Streetlights were darkened and automobiles were required to pull over to the side of the road and switch off their headlights, then to wait until the drill was complete. These blackouts persisted for the duration of the war.

As the war continued, certain food items came to be in short supply. Soon each household was given ration books. The total amount of stamps depended on the number of people in the family and their ages. Certain things could be purchased without any rationing, while other items were limited and could only be purchased with government-issued ration stamps. Items such as sugar, flour, eggs, coffee, butter, and most meats were being sent overseas to feed the troops, so what remained in the States was strictly regulated. Very little meat was available, so in many homes horsemeat was on the menu. Other items such as nylons, gasoline, and rubber were also in short supply. People were required to save much of their domestic waste, such as tin cans, rubber seals and gaskets, and torn stockings. These were collected and recycled for use in the war effort.

I was eight years old when the war began, and it was strange as a child to comprehend the magnitude of what was happening around the world. We would hear news reports on the radio or read them in the newspaper, and there were also newsreels at the movie theater giving updates on the war as well as propaganda to embolden our patriotic resolve. We were already accustomed to food shortages during the Depression, so the rationing was not considerably different.

Many young men enlisted or were drafted into the military. Uncle Pete was drafted into the Navy Engineer Corps and stationed in Australia. He would write to Kay and me every week and sometimes send us small presents. The trinkets we received from faraway places had a mystical effect on us.

Uncle Carm also joined the navy in 1943, after the tragic death of his two-year-old son, Carmine. Little Carmine was the light of my uncle's life. Every day when the factory whistle would blow announcing the one-hour lunch break, little Carmine would run to the window and shout, "Daddy come! Daddy come!" Uncle Carm would come home for lunch and play with his son and shower him with affection.

Then just before Carmine's second birthday, his mother, Aunt Eleanor, went to Newburgh to buy him a pair of shoes as a birthday present. While Aunt Prov was watching him, he started playing on the back stoop with the empty milk bottles he found in the case for the milkman to pick up the next day. Carmine was taking the bottles out of the box and putting them back in when he tripped over a raised section of concrete, then fell on the bottle, which broke and severed a vein in his neck.

As Aunt Eleanor was coming home, she saw the family car speeding past in the opposite direction with the horn blasting. She immediately knew that something was wrong. When she arrived at the hospital, little Carmine was already gone. My uncle was devastated. He no longer came home for lunch. Instead, he went to the cemetery where the soil was still soft on his son's grave. He would find a stick and probe the dirt until he could feel the casket in which his son lay. This continued for weeks until my broken uncle could bear it no longer. He joined the navy and was gone for two years in the South Pacific. When he returned home, he was able to cope with the loss of his son. He and my aunt had three more children and lived together for sixty more years.

In our neighborhood we began to see little flags appear in the windows of houses. They had a white background with a red border. On the background was a blue star representing each young man from that home serving in the military. As the war continued and young men were becoming casualties, the stars began to change. Seeing a home with a gold star on the banner signified that a son from that family had been killed in action. A woman from Gate Street in our neighborhood, Mrs. Ghebbia, had a son who was killed in Italy. I'll never forget her shrieks when the service men came to the door to inform her of his loss. She wore black from that day on and never came out of mourning.

The United States was at war with Japan and Germany, but also with Italy, which had allied itself with the Axis powers. When President Roosevelt signed Executive Order 9066, it identified the seven hundred thousand Italians living in the United States who were not citizens as enemy aliens. This didn't directly affect my family since my grandparents were deceased and my father and his siblings were American born. But rumors began to circulate that some families were being visited by the police or military, who asked them to surrender any radio transmitters, firearms, and cameras.

Young men who were born in Italy and weren't American citizens were conscripted into the military, being given the choice to "join or be deported." Some people, Italian and German too, were required to carry an identification card stamped "enemy alien." A great deal of shame was associated with these regulations, and no one spoke of them at the time.

As a little girl, I was quite oblivious to any policies directed at people like my family. I do recall that at the post office and the train station there were posters with caricatures of Hitler, Hirohito, and Mussolini that stated in bold print, "Don't Speak the Enemy's Language." My family had not really spoken Sicilian since my dad's grandmother died, but my uncles and aunts would speak it among themselves at times. Having seen the posters, I wondered if they might get in trouble.

Growing up during the war years was sometimes frightening. It was hard to understand when the radio would speak of troop movements in faraway places or the newsreels would report on battles in the South Pacific or Europe. How close were these places with strange names like Okinawa or Normandy? Eventually we received the news that the war in Europe and, soon after, the war with Japan was over. It was a great relief to everyone, and I was especially thankful that there would be no more blackouts. The years immediately following the war was a season of readjustment. The government's rationing program came to a close. By the end of that year, sugar was the only commodity still being rationed. That restriction finally ended in June 1947. Plenty of other goods remained in short supply for months after the war, thanks to years of pent-up demand.

It was common to see men in military uniforms everywhere. They wore their regimentals as a badge of honor when going to the theater, into stores, and even to church. Every weekend, two or three weddings were taking place in the neighborhood, usually young couples who had postponed their nuptials for the sake of world peace. I was entering my last year of grade school when our landlord, Mr. Hughes, told us he needed our apartment for his daughter who was marrying a returning veteran. So we moved to South Clover Street, where I was living when I met Tommy two years later, and I lived there until we were married.

ELEVEN

Transitions

My sophomore year of high school proved to be significantly more frustrating than my freshman year. Not only was I unable to enroll in any courses for the secretarial program, but I was now two years behind the other girls registered. Acquiring the necessary classes for a diploma in this course of study would be virtually impossible.

When I couldn't register for any secretarial courses in the fall term, I hoped that the spring semester would be different. It wasn't. So, I was faced with a decision. Either I could trudge along taking random courses and graduate with a generic diploma, or I could press on and take whatever secretarial courses were available and hopefully graduate before my thirtieth birthday. I discussed this with my parents again, and with their permission, at the end of the school year, I officially withdrew from school and began working at the pocketbook factory with my father.

Kay was able to complete her studies and graduated in June, though she didn't attend the commencement ceremony. Kay had completed her course study in December and was ready to graduate in January, but the school didn't allow midterm graduation and the only way Kay could attend the ceremony was to take several superfluous classes and await the end-of-year ritual with the entire class.

Kay wasn't willing to do so since she already had employment arranged at Domestic Finance on Market Street. She chose to begin her career rather than prolong her high school experience. My mother was disappointed since she had never attended a high school graduation before, having only finished sixth grade herself. Now, with her oldest daughter refusing to attend the ceremony and her youngest daughter dropping out of school, she would have to wait until her first grandchild finished high school to experience a commencement ceremony.

Tommy also graduated in the class of 1949. He attended his graduation alone, without anyone from his family present. After the commencement exercises, he went home to his empty house and fixed himself something to eat, then went out to meet whomever he might find at the candy store.

Summer was very different this year since I was now working with my dad at the factory. My job was to cut the dangling threads from certain areas on the finished pocket-books—the handles, the seams, and the edges. The women operating the sewing machines would leave the long threads hanging when they stitched the purses, and my job was to cut the threads off. My position was considered a finishing job, one of the last steps before collecting the handbags, packing them, and shipping them out. The work was boring and the days were long, but I was paid sixty cents per hour, which was a good salary for a novice unskilled laborer. Kay was also working full-time, and because of her secretarial skills she was making one dollar per hour, which was an excellent salary for a young woman in 1949. With our jobs we were able to contribute to the household income so our family's financial burdens were diminished.

Working five days a week at the factory was at times onerous, but the most difficult part was rising early enough to complete my morning routine, make the long walk to the factory, and be there by the time the whistle blew signaling the start of the workday. Anyone who hadn't punched the time clock and wasn't at their station when the whistle sounded would be docked.

My parents, as always, took it upon themselves to assist me in acclimating to my new situation in life. My mother would pack lunch for my father and me so there was one less chore to accomplish each morning. The walk to work with my dad each day was a joy. He was always so cheerful at this time of day and kept the conversation going the entire way to work. At lunchtime he would find me, and we would sit outside and enjoy lunch together. I took my morning and afternoon breaks with some of the older women on the sewing floor since we only had a ten-minute respite and there was no one my age working on the mezzanine. It was tedious work, and I was lonely for someone my age to talk to, but I focused on the task before me and determined to be the best finisher on the factory floor.

I loved the weekends when I could see my friends and spend time with the gang. There were, of course, the Saturday chores, but I enjoyed working with my family to put everything in order for my mother, who labored long hours to maintain the house. There were still the weekend sporting events and dances, and outings with the gang to the pool or roller-skating rink. The city once again was alive with its street festivals and neighborhood block parties.

Our family's Sunday picnic regimen restarted, officially launching with the Memorial Day holiday. Everything was the same as in previous years, with one exception: I now saw them all in a new light. I felt more grateful for the times of recreation, entertainment, and repose. Events and occasions that I'd enjoyed before were increasingly special to me as I realized that I no longer looked presumptuously at their value but appreciated the occasion as an opportunity to cherish the time spent with those I loved. Time would pass, the weekend would soon be over, and the requirements of life would preempt the joys of living. Nevertheless, the weekends proved to be a renaissance for my soul, empowering me for the subsequent week of labor.

Tommy and I spent most Friday nights together at the movies or taking a walk down Main Street. Daddy would go to play darts at the local tavern, and Kay was always out. This frequently left my mother by herself at the start of the weekend, so Tommy and I would spend time with her before going to the movies. Or we would skip the movies and just pass the night playing dominos with Mom. She enjoyed the company and the opportunity to spend time with Tommy. She was becoming more comfortable with him, and he was noticeably less self-protective and shielding.

Still, there was something unsettled about Tommy. He seemed lost, uncertain of what direction in life to follow. Since graduation, he had been working odd jobs around town but had no steady employment. He wasn't working with his father, nor had he begun to apprentice as a brick-layer. When I asked him about this, he was evasive, saying only that he had some things to decide. I was uncertain what he meant, but he was a private fellow and extremely stingy when sharing personal information.

June ushered in my sixteenth birthday. My mother had always given Kay and me a birthday party. This was very important to her since birthday celebrations had not been permitted by her grandfather, who claimed they were a frivolous waste of money and that he already provided everything that the girls needed. The grandmother feared him and would not go against his mandates.

On one occasion she surprised my mother and her two sisters telling them to go and invite all their friends to come over for their birthday party that afternoon. The girls were shocked and asked, "What about grandpa?" The grandmother simply responded that everything would be completed before he came home that day. So, the girls left the house and invited their friends. When they returned home, they saw decorations, smelled cake baking and discovered three gifts on the table. They were amazed that their grandmother would go against the grandfather's commands and had so purposely planned this event.

Their friends all came and celebrated their birthdays, but too soon the grandmother announced that everyone would need to leave, and she and the girls cleaned the house and hid the gifts. It was a secret the girls and their grandmother would keep forever, and it was the only birthday celebration my mother ever had. Therefore, she was determined that her daughters would have a birthday party every year.

This year was a special party for me, my sweet sixteen birthday. My mother put forth maximum effort baking cakes and cookies, decorating the house, and providing an atmosphere of festivity both sumptuous and resplendent. There were games with competition rivaling Olympic events, and songs sung from sheet music we had purchased with voices rising in four-part harmony, occasionally in tune. Everyone was in attendance, except one. Tommy didn't show.

No one seemed to notice, but I was very upset. We had argued several days before the party, but I'd presumed that he would attend despite that. Yet the party continued for several hours and Tommy never appeared. My mother realized that he was missing and noticed my attempts to show no reaction to his absence. My mother could read my thoughts like the evening newspaper and was preparing to answer my questions about Tommy's actions when the party was over.

After everyone had gone home, and my mother, Kay, and I were cleaning, the doorbell rang. I assumed someone had forgotten something, but when I answered the door, there stood Tommy Serino.

After a few moments of silence, I said, "Well?"

"I, uh, I wanted to give you the birthday gift that I bought for you," Tommy stammered and then held out the small, gift-wrapped package.

I didn't reach for it. "Where were you, Tommy? You knew it was my birthday. Where were you? Everyone was here. I don't know what to say to you." My emotions had clouded my thoughts, making me ramble.

"Look," Tommy said, "I know I should've been here and I'm sorry. Sometimes being around a large group of people just gets to me. I feel closed in and I just want to run." He was being unusually open with his feelings, so I didn't interrupt. "Doris, I like you. I really, really care for you, but I don't always know what to do about it. I'm sorry that I missed your birthday party. I don't know what else to say."

I sighed. "I forgive you, Tommy, and I really care for you too. That's why I felt so bad that you didn't show on an occasion that was so special to me." I wasn't trying to make him feel guilty, but I wanted him to know that his actions hurt me.

"I understand, Doris, and I'm sorry. It won't happen again."

"No, it won't. You only turn sixteen once, and you missed it," I said with a smile.

He breathed a sigh of relief.

"So, you had a gift for me?" I said, now that all was well again.

"Yes. Here." Tommy held out the present.

My mother came to the door as I was opening it. "Come in, Tommy, and have a piece of cake." It was more of a command than a request, so Tommy came in and sat down to a piece of my birthday cake and watched me open his gift.

Kay glared at him and said, "I wouldn't let you off that easy."

"Get in the kitchen and finish putting the dishes away," my mother scolded.

When I opened the box, inside was an ornate, delicate musical powder box. "Oh my," I exclaimed. "It's beautiful." I turned the box over and wound it up. The box began to play "It's Too Soon to Know," and we sat in silence while the music box filled the air with a melody that had come to have great significance to us.

When the song was over, we sat for a moment, then Tommy tenderly grasped my hand. With no words exchanged, we shared a silent bond.

In the beginning of August, the sweltering city had begun to trudge through the "dog days" of summer. The factory floor was oppressively hot, and the paucity of fresh air was stifling. July had produced several days with temperatures over one hundred degrees. Now in the first week of August we were experiencing another heat wave with temperatures in triple digits. The factory floor was intolerable, and several women fainted at their workstations.

Consequently, the foreman brought out four large pedestal fans and placed them in the corners of the mezzanine. The circulation of the minimal air present in the building was some relief, but the intensity of the noise generated by the fans made dialogue impossible. Floor captains were giving written instructions on scraps of paper, forgoing all attempts at verbal commands.

Tommy was now eighteen, his birthday having passed without any acknowledgment, at the end of July. We had been arguing frequently over the past month, so I didn't see him for his birthday. He'd been acting distant and reticent, so I gave him a wide berth to allow him to resolve the issues he was wrestling with. I hadn't seen him all week and admittedly was becoming somewhat concerned.

The weekend arrived, and Friday night came and went with no word from Tommy. I went to the movies with Kay, who conveniently had no date for the evening. Saturday morning my family and I were completely engrossed in our weekly cleaning ritual when a knock on the door surprised us all. It was unusual for neighbors to visit on a Saturday morning; generally, the time to call on friends and family was in the late afternoon or evening.

My father went to the door and opened it, then I heard him say, "Come in, Mr. Serino. Will you have some coffee?"

"No, thank you," he said in heavily accented English. "I come to see Doris."

At hearing my name, I entered the kitchen to find Tommy's father standing beside the table. He wore a light sport coat, a perfectly pressed white shirt, and a recently blocked fedora. He was not a tall man—several inches shorter than Tommy—but he was solid, and his broad shoulders were clearly noticeable despite the sport coat.

When he saw me, he took my hand and greeted me warmly, "Hello, Doris. How are you, honey?" He was a charismatic man who spoke English with a thick Italian accent, yet with great aplomb. His face was dark, more brown than swarthy, and as he spoke a broad smile revealed beautiful white teeth and a welcoming expression.

"I'm fine, Mr. Serino. Is Tommy okay?" I asked, cutting directly to the presumed reason for Mr. Serino's visit. I hadn't seen Tommy in over a week and now his father had appeared for an arbitrary visit. My fears were mounting that something serious had occurred.

"Yes, he's fine," he responded, attempting to be reassuring. "But that's why I come. Tommy joined the marines. He leave today. He just go. He go Camp LeJeune in North Carolina. I think he don't tell you too."

I was stunned, numb, and unable to respond. This was so completely unexpected. Tommy had never mentioned the marines before.

My mother approached the table with a steaming cup of fresh coffee and placed it in front of Mr. Serino and asked if she could fix him some breakfast. I understood this as an attempt to give me a moment to recoil from the news.

"No, thank you, Mrs. Messina. That's very kind." Tommy's father then looked back to me. "Sit down, Doris."

We both sat down, and he didn't let go of my hand. "I

find out yesterday. Tommy say, 'I joined marines. I leave tomorrow. I will not be home until basic training is over.' And that's it! That's all he say. He no tell nobody. He just go."

I finally found my voice. "Well, thank you for coming over to tell me. Tommy never said a word to me, but I haven't seen him for over a week, and this explains why. So, I guess that's it, then."

"No, it's no good. You nice girl. Tommy should tell you first."

Truthfully, while I was surprised and hurt, I wasn't angry. After all, it wasn't the first time Tommy and I had broken up, although there appeared to be a finality this time. "Well, thank you for telling me, Mr. Serino. I have to finish my chores now." Leaving my parents in the kitchen with Tommy's father, I returned to my assigned duty. It was my turn to clean the bathroom, and I would enjoy the privacy this task provided.

The news of Tommy's departure and my apparent availability traveled quickly around town, because in the following week I had more invitations to the movies and to escort me to the dance or for a soda at Barney's than ever before. I did accept a few invitations and had several dates over the next couple of weeks. Yet Tommy was always in my thoughts. Recovering from our relationship's end was more difficult than I'd presumed. Tommy was a strange and complicated person, but I'd grown more attached to him than I realized. I guess I wasn't expecting such a sudden ending to our partnership. As abruptly as it began, it was over.

With mid-August came temperatures that were more seasonal, so life at the factory was not as oppressive. Daddy and I were walking home each night as before, but since

Mr. Serino's visit he had been much more tender and attentive. It was as though he wanted to bear some of the burden I carried but was unsure how to do that.

One night when we entered the house, Mom was in the kitchen and the aroma of fried potatoes and sausage filled the house. "Alice, we're home," my father called.

"I heard you, Joe. You don't have to shout. Doris, there's a letter for you on the table."

A letter from whom? I wondered. I walked to the table and there sat a clean white envelope bearing the name "Miss Doris Messina," my address, and a canceled three-cent stamp. I picked up the envelope and looked at the return address. There was no name, but it was from Camp LeJeune, North Carolina. Tommy.

I rushed to my room to read it privately. Kay was still at work and wouldn't return for about thirty minutes. I pulled the letter out of the previously opened envelope with shaking hands. There was no way I could anticipate what he was about to say, but I felt that this letter would determine the direction of our relationship. I read the letter aloud in a hushed tone so that I alone could hear what I read.

"My dearest Doris. Since I left Poughkeepsie, I have thought of nothing but you. I miss you more than I ever expected was possible. I am afraid that by leaving as suddenly as I did that you would hate me and never want to see me again. That is something I couldn't bear. I love you. Now I have said it. I miss you and I love you and I never want to be apart from you. I have signed up for a three-year tour of duty in the marines, but I can come home for a visit every weekend once my two-month basic training is over.

"I want to ask you to wait for me until I finish my service then we can have a future together. We need to be together. Please write back to me soon and tell me that you'll wait for me. I couldn't bear it if you said no." It was signed "All my love, Tom." At the top of the letter in the right-hand margin was the title of the song from the Charioteers, "It's Too Soon to Know."

I didn't know how to react. I was stunned. I was relieved. I was happy. I was afraid to trust, to believe that Tommy was even capable of committing to a long-term partnership. I decided not to answer him until later when I had a chance to really think about what "waiting for him" actually entailed. With the letter back in the envelope and placed in my top dresser drawer, I returned to the kitchen just as Kay came home, which meant there would be no discussion about the letter with my parents at this time. For this I was thankful.

Little conversation happened after dinner while Mom, Kay, and I were cleaning the dishes and organizing the kitchen as Mom's workspace for tomorrow. When all was in order, my family retired to the parlor, where each night we listened to the radio as my father read the evening paper. This evening, rather than listen to my favorite programs, I withdrew to my bedroom and retrieved Tommy's letter. I had paper, a pen, and an envelope ready to answer his question but was uncertain how I should respond.

Suddenly Kay entered the bedroom. She noticed that I was preparing to write a letter and asked if the letter I received today was from Tommy. It turned out she already knew the answer since Mom had opened the letter before I got home from work. "Yes, it was from Tommy," I said simply.

She didn't ask to read the letter, and I didn't offer the opportunity.

"I don't think you should give this guy any more

chances, Doris," she told me firmly but not unkindly. "Every time you do, he pulls something like this and hurts you all over again."

"Kay, I know you're looking out for me, but there's something very sincere about Tommy Serino," I replied. "I think he's just confused and unsure which direction to go to find what he needs."

Kay shook her head, now angry. "What kind of life would you have with a guy like that? He runs hot and cold. One minute he's all apologetic and the next instant he runs away."

I giggled to myself. "It would be an interesting life, of that I'm certain. But I think he just needs the assurance that someone genuinely loves him."

"And you love him?" Kay asked sardonically.

It wasn't until that moment that I realized I did in fact love him. I loved Tommy Serino, and I believed I always would love him. "I believe I do, Kay," I said softly.

She stared at me for a few moments, then spoke more calmly. "I think you're crazy. But if he hurts you again, I swear I'll beat him with a stick. You just be cautious, little sister. And be sure to let Tommy Serino know that big sister is watching him."

I smiled at her care and concern. "Thanks, Kay," I said as she left the room.

My conversation with Kay made me recognize that my feelings for Tommy were deeper than I had realized and that I would be willing to wait for him, no matter how long it might take.

I was now ready to write my letter.

TWELVE
Tommy's First Visit

E very day I received a letter from Tommy, and every night I would write a letter in return. Tommy was able to express in writing what he couldn't articulate in person. With each new letter I saw a little deeper into his heart and mind. He was able to convey his hope as well as his fears, to reveal his insecurities openly and entrust me with thoughts that he'd never divulged to anyone. With each new correspondence I was growing closer to him, and Tommy was becoming more confident to share with me without fear of rejection.

One Saturday afternoon in mid-September, I had a surprise visitor. My mother had gone across the street to visit with Hattie, Daddy had gone to the Italian Center to play cards, and Kay was shopping on Main Street with Irma Patera, so I was at home alone. I was waiting for the mailman to come so I could post my latest correspondence to Tommy and, hopefully, receive another letter from him.

When the doorbell rang, I assumed it was the postman making an earlier appearance than usual. But when I opened the door, there stood Eleanor DiPilco. Eleanor had never come to my house before, and truthfully, we weren't friends.

"Hi, Doris," she said after a moment of awkward silence. "May I come in?"

I stepped back to let her in. "Of course, Eleanor. Come on into the kitchen. Can I get something for you?" I tried to be as cordial as possible, but also wondered why she was here. It obviously wasn't a social visit.

Eleanor sat down at the table, and I took the seat at the head of the table with my back to the doorway. "So, what's on your mind, Eleanor?" I asked.

"I wanted to talk to you about Tommy."

Just what I'd expected. "What about him?"

"Well… as you know, Tommy and I have known each other since we were young. Our mothers are friends, and we've spent a great deal of time together. I know that Tommy cares for me, and frankly I care for him very much."

Uncomfortable, I squirmed in my chair.

"As you must realize, every time you and Tommy broke up, he always came back to me," she went on. "I've always been his anchor, always been faithful to him."

I could feel my blood pressure rising and a flush come over my face.

Eleanor was fully engaged at this point and continued to state her case. "With Tommy in the marines now, he's away from both of us, but I got a letter from him, so I know that he still cares for me." She swallowed. "Look, Doris, I don't want any trouble. I'm here because I believe Tommy really cares for me and, well, honestly, you're just confusing him. So, I'd like you to do the honorable thing and give Tommy up. Please just step aside and let us get on with our relationship. You're a nice person, Doris, and I'm sure you know how much Tommy cares for me. Therefore, I'm asking you to do what is right."

I couldn't believe the unmitigated gall of this girl, coming into my home and making such bold demands. I opened my mouth, ready to go toe to toe with Eleanor and argue my case, to point out to her where her assumptions were distorted and her conclusions biased. Suddenly I had a better idea.

I excused myself for a moment, went to my room, and retrieved the shoe box of letters I'd received from Tommy over the past few weeks. When I returned to the kitchen, I placed it on the table in front of Eleanor.

"What is this?" she asked.

"Lift the lid and look inside," I replied.

When she removed the lid, her expression made it clear that she recognized the letters, the handwriting, and the familiar return address of Camp LeJeune. "Take any letter you want, Eleanor, and read it," I told her.

She withdrew a letter and opened it. As she began to read, the color drained from her face. Every letter began with the salutation, "My dearest Doris," and at the top was the title of the Charioteers' song "It's Too Soon to Know." The content of each letter affirmed Tommy's growing love and affection for me and his hopes to share a future with me.

Eleanor placed the letter back in the envelope and returned it to the box.

"Take another one," I said.

She dutifully took another from the box, removed it from the envelope, and read it. Then she put it back in the envelope, replaced it in the box, and looked at me. After drawing a breath and letting it out, she said quietly,

"Well, I guess we know who he wants now, don't we." Eleanor rose from her chair, held her head high, and without a word walked to the front door. After opening the door, she turned toward me and said, "Goodbye, Doris," then left.

It was mid-October when Tommy was able to come home for the first time. I received a letter from him on Wednesday that he had liberty for the coming weekend and he would be returning home sometime on Friday night. He couldn't predict his arrival time since he'd be hitchhiking from North Carolina, but his departure time was four in the evening.

I was beyond excited. This would be the first time I'd seen him since he left in August.

When Friday night came, I could hardly sleep. It was a warm night, and the window was open. I attended to every sound, but the street was exceptionally quiet. I heard the chimes on Nativity Church strike three and began to wonder if he would make it back at all.

I must have drifted off to sleep because I dreamed that I heard him whisper my name. I smiled at the sound of his voice and thought how pleasant it would be to hear it once again. Suddenly I did hear it again. "Doris!" I lay still on my bed, now fully awake, wondering if my imagination was taking advantage of my anticipation, when I heard for the third time, "Doris!"

There was no mistaking the voice. It was Tommy. He was home. I leaped from the bed and ran to the window. There he stood on the sidewalk in his khaki-colored marine uniform calling my name in a loud whisper.

"Tommy!" I shrieked. "I'll unlock the door. Come around front." I quickly wrapped my housecoat around me, bounded down the stairs, and threw open the door.

With one motion he gathered me in his arms, spun me around, and kissed me.

I was elated. "When did you get home, Tommy?"

"Just now," he responded. "I haven't been to my house yet. I came here first."

"How long did it take you to get here? Did you actually leave at four?" I asked.

"Yes. But I couldn't get a ride at first. Then I got a long ride all the way to New Jersey. After that, it took four or five different drivers to get here. The last guy was only going to Peekskill but decided to take me all the way here instead. Boy, have I missed you. Did you miss me? I can't believe I'm finally seeing you again. It seems like years since we were together." Tommy was overflowing with conversation. I'd never seen him so talkative before.

"Are you hungry?" I asked. "Can I get you something to eat?" Now understanding just how far away Tommy actually was at Camp LeJeune, I knew he had to be hungry and tired.

"No, thanks. I'm going to go home and try and catch a few hours' sleep. I'll come back in the morning." With that, he took me in his arms again, kissed me goodnight, and was gone.

Despite my lack of sleep, I arose early in the morning and started on my chores before breakfast. I knew Tommy would be here sometime this morning, and Mom was a stickler about completing chores before going anywhere.

We were just finishing breakfast when Tommy arrived. When the doorbell rang, I jumped up and ran down the stairs to open the door. Tommy stood there in his uniform and with a fist full of flowers. I threw my arms around him and kissed his cheek. "Come on, everyone is upstairs."

We scaled the stairs, Tommy taking two at a time and my small feet doing double time. We entered the kitchen hand in hand, and I said, "Well, here he is."

My mother rose from the table. "Good morning, Tommy. Can I fix you some breakfast? Here, let me take those flowers and put them in water."

Daddy extended his hand to Tommy and said, "Welcome back, son. How was the journey home?"

"Thank you, Mr. Messina. The trip was a little longer than I anticipated. Thankfully I was wearing my uniform. I think that got me most of my rides."

"Well, since the war I think people have a new respect for our boys in the service," Daddy responded. It dawned on me at that moment that my father had begun to look at Tommy in a new light, seeing him as a respectable military man rather than a street urchin. "How was your first few weeks in boot camp?" My father had never been in the military, but from his brothers and some young men at the factory, he was familiar with the severity of the initial stages of military training.

"In truth, sir, they kicked my butt good," Tommy said.

My father chuckled. "Well, you probably needed a good kick in the behind."

Tommy smiled. "I believe I did, Mr. Messina."

My mother placed a hot cup of coffee in front of Tommy, then asked me, "What are you kids planning on doing today?"

Her question had two connotations. First, she could not understand how an unscheduled day was any more than a waste of time. Second, and more importantly, she knew that an unplanned day could result in other unplanned events, something she desperately wanted her daughters to avoid.

"I thought we'd walk up Union Street to see if any of the gang is there," Tommy told her. "Then we'll see if anything is going on at Lincoln Center. I'll have Doris home before dinnertime, because we'll be taking in an early movie tonight and will need time to get ready. We'll come back here after, and then I think we both could use a little more sleep than we had last night."

My mother seemed satisfied with his detailed plans and turned to me. "Have you finished your chores?"

"Yes, Ma," I answered. "I just need about fifteen minutes to get ready."

Kay, who'd been quiet as she stood at the sink filling it with water, said, "You'd better settle in, Tommy. This will be the longest fifteen minutes you've ever seen."

I stuck my tongue out at Kay, then smiled at her, knowing she was trying hard to give Tommy another chance. As I hurried from the room, I heard my mother instruct, "You boys go in the parlor so I can clean up this kitchen."

I took less than fifteen minutes to get ready, then went to the parlor where my father and Tommy were talking. When they looked at me, both became silent.

Tommy was the first to speak. "You look beautiful, Doris."

I blushed, having received the coveted acknowledgment.

"You kids have fun," Daddy said. "You'll be back for dinner, right?"

"Yes, sir," Tommy assured him.

I went into the kitchen, where Mom was rearranging items in the cupboard, having just removed the necessary supplies for her Saturday baking and meal preparation, while Kay was sitting at the table filing recipe cards. "I'll see you guys later," I said and bent over to smell one of the flowers Tommy brought, which were now displayed proudly in the middle of the table.

"Be good," Mom replied.

Kay smiled, then stuck her tongue out at me and smiled again.

I winked at her as I left the kitchen.

It was a beautiful day. The sun was shining brightly and the crisp autumn breeze, although cool, was refreshing. We walked up Union Street hand in hand, with Tommy sharing his experiences over the last few months. He seemed genuinely content, more satisfied than I'd ever seen him. It was as if in the marines he had found the family he'd always wanted.

As we approached the candy store, we encountered Bobby Heller, Frank Bitzko, and Gerald Knowl. When they saw us, they began goading Tommy.

"Look at this! They'll give a uniform to anybody anymore."

"Now I've seen everything. Doris is walking with the meter maid."

"No way. That ugly face can only belong to Tommy Serino."

"You wish you were as pretty as me, Bitzko!" Tommy responded.

This verbal volleying was followed by handshakes, hugs, and back slaps all around, and of course a kiss on the cheek from each young man for me. "Doris, you look so beautiful. I don't know what you see in this guy here," Bobby said.

"He's right, Doris. You could marry Frank Sinatra looking like that," Gerald added.

"Yeah, she's with me, guys, and that ain't going to change," Tommy fired back. Then he asked, "Where is everyone today?"

"This is it," Frank answered. "Everyone else is working today."

"How come you aren't working, Bobby?" Tommy asked, awaiting his response with a witty remark.

"Oh, you didn't hear?" Gerald said. "Bobby works for Culligan Water Softener Company now. He's in the big leagues, a nine-to-five guy."

"Aww, cut it out, guys," Bobby replied. "I just install the units right now."

"Yeah, but he's planning on owning the company in a few years," Frank added.

"So nobody is down at Lincoln Center or Eastman Park today?" Tommy sounded disappointed that he wouldn't be seeing the whole gang.

Bobby shrugged. "I doubt it. Whoever isn't working probably has responsibilities at home. I don't know what anyone is doing tonight. Lately the guys have been going separate ways, what with jobs and girlfriends and everything."

It appeared that things had been changing for all of us since many of the guys and gals had graduated last June.

"Well, Doris," Tommy said, "I guess we'll just walk up Main Street and see what's going on uptown."

I smiled at him. "That's fine with me. As long as we're together."

My response elicited a barrage of cat calls and taunts whose volume far exceeded the number of young men present, and which continued as we preceded down Perry Street and left the heckling boys behind.

The afternoon passed quickly, and soon Tommy and I

were back at my house. He stopped at my front door and said, "I'll be back around six thirty to pick you up for the early show. That new John Wayne movie, *She Wore a Yellow Ribbon*, is playing."

I was surprised. "Wait. Aren't you staying for dinner, Tommy?"

"No. I've got to get home and change, but I'll be back to get you, so be ready." Tommy then kissed me goodbye and was off.

I should have been accustomed to his abrupt exits, but they still confounded me. I walked up the stairs and went inside just as my mother was putting dinner on the table.

"Go wash up, Doris. Dinner is ready." Only four plates sat on the table, so my mother had anticipated Tommy's absence.

When I returned from the bathroom, she asked, "Did Tommy go home?"

"Yes."

"He's a strange one, that boy," Mom mumbled to herself. "I guess he thinks I'm going to poison him or something."

Tommy was back promptly at six thirty. He had changed out of his uniform and into a casual outfit of slacks and a shirt. We enjoyed the movie and afterward went back to my house to spend some time with my mother. As usual, Kay was out and my father was playing darts in the local tavern. Mom had baked an apple pie, several in fact, and we enjoyed pie and coffee with her while listening to *Fireside Theater* on the radio in the parlor.

I was having a hard time staying awake and dozed off a few times despite the action and suspense unfolding on the radio. When the program was over, Tommy said, "I'd better get going, Doris, and let you get some sleep."

"I'm not tired," I protested.

"No," my mother chided. "Those naps you took during the program must have revived you."

Tommy laughed, and I poked him in the ribs. "Don't laugh, you'll just encourage her," I reprimanded.

Tommy stood to leave. "I'll see you at mass tomorrow morning, Doris. And goodnight, Mrs. Messina."

"Goodnight, Tommy. Will I see you before you leave?"

"I'll make it a point to stop by after church."

I rose to walk him to the door. "I had a lot of fun with you today," I said when we got to the bottom of the stairs. "I really wish you didn't have to leave already tomorrow."

"We have all day tomorrow, though," he assured me. "The train doesn't leave until five o'clock, and I expect to be back next weekend."

"Really?" I squealed.

"Yes. Now that basic training is over, I should be able to come home every weekend." He had been waiting to surprise me with this bit of information, and he succeeded.

"Oh my goodness, Tommy, that's wonderful."

"Well, get some rest, Doris. I'll see you at the nine o'clock mass tomorrow. Goodnight." With that, he kissed me and was gone.

I went back upstairs to the parlor, where Mom was waiting for me.

"So, what did you do today, Doris?" she asked.

I recounted all the details of the day and enjoyed reliving them for my mother. She listened intently, experiencing every event with me—our conversations, our interactions with friends, and our general gaiety of sharing even the smallest moments with each other.

"That's nice," she said when I finished. "Now why don't you get ready for bed. You didn't get much sleep last night, and frankly, neither did I, and you know that Tommy will be here bright and early tomorrow."

"Okay, Mom. Goodnight."

"Goodnight, Doris."

Tommy arrived early the next morning, choosing to walk to church with Kay and me rather than meet us there. We walked in a few minutes before mass began, which gave Tommy just enough time to reconnect with the rest of the gang who we hadn't seen yesterday. The girls took their places in the pews while the boys stood together in the rear of the church near the narthex.

The mass seemed unusually long that morning, with Father Ashfalg croaking out the prayers in Latin and Miss Laurena Light pummeling the organ with musical embellishments for every hymn. When the time for the collection arrived, Father Ashfalg took the basket in hand and walked the length and breadth of the church, gathering coins and bills from the faithful.

When he arrived in the back of the church where the young men assembled, he examined each one, looking over the glasses perched on his nose. If he was not satisfied with the amount of money they placed in the collection, he would strike them with the basket and clear his throat loudly. Father Ashfalg had an uncanny knowledge of the intimate details of the lives of his congregation. Each night he sat on his front porch and watched over the neighborhood like a guardian angel, making mental notes of every observance.

As he approached Billy Reevey with the collection, Billy reached into his pocket and placed a dollar bill in the basket. Father Ashfalg struck Billy with the basket and announced loudly, "Billy Reevey, if you can throw ten dollars over the bar last night, you can throw ten dollars in the collection."

Billy obediently reached into his pocket and placed a more appropriate amount in the basket, thus soliciting a gratified nod from the priest.

After mass, we all gathered on the sidewalk outside the church. The conversations were many and varied and included anyone and no one. Tommy approached Kay and I and said, "Are you ready, girls? Let's get you home. First, let's stop at Honey's Bakery on the corner for some crumb buns. We'll surprise your mom."

As we entered the house, we were enveloped by the aroma of Mom's Sunday sauce, which she'd started early that morning so it would be ready for dinner at two in the afternoon. We gave the confectionery to my mother, who put on a pot of coffee and arranged the breakfast buns on a serving platter.

Kay and I went to change from our Sunday clothes into something more casual, while Tommy headed for the parlor, where my father was reading the newspaper. Soon my mother called us all to the kitchen, where the table was set with crumb buns, sugar buns, jelly donuts, and hard rolls. A bowl of seasonal fruit—apples and pears—and fresh coffee were also available.

We each took a seat at the table, and before taking any food or drink those of us who had received Holy Communion took a glass of water. We were all hungry since no food was permitted after midnight in preparation for the Eucharist at Sunday morning mass. After drinking the water and cleansing our palates from the remnants of the consecrated comestible, we were ready to consume the more common confections. That day I discovered Tommy's enduring love for crumb buns, especially those made at Honey's Bakery.

"So what are you planning to do today, Doris?" Mom asked, initiating her review of our itinerary.

"Well, nothing is open today since it's Sunday, so there isn't much to do," Tommy answered.

This was an unsatisfactory answer for my mother, so she began her suggestions of acceptable activities. "Well, your uncle Carm, aunt Eleanor, and the kids are coming up this afternoon for dinner."

"I'm afraid I won't be able to stay for dinner, Mrs. Messina," Tommy said. "I have to go home and pack my things to make the five o'clock train. Plus, I haven't seen my mother yet, so I'm hoping to see her before I go."

Mom's eyes widened. "You haven't seen your mother yet?"

"No, ma'am. She wasn't home yesterday, and this morning I left for church before she was up. I'll try to find her this afternoon, though."

"I see," was all my mother said.

After breakfast, Tommy and I retired to the parlor while my father helped my mother in the kitchen and Kay went to see Irma Patera before dinner. Tommy then posed a question that perplexed me at the time. "Doris, I'd like you to do me a favor this week," he began.

"Of course. What can I do for you?" I asked innocently.

"I'd like you to go to my house and visit my mother sometime this week. Would you do that for me, please?"

"Well, of course. I'd love to meet your mother."

Though I responded enthusiastically, Tommy remained sober and serious. "It might not be what you expect. My family is different than yours. However, I think it's time you got to know my family." He seemed concerned about my encounter with his family and how I might react to meeting them.

I knew this was important to him, so I promised to visit that week before he returned on Friday.

A great burden seemed lifted from his shoulders now that this was arranged, and he began to relax once again. We passed the time talking and laughing, and Tommy helped my dad set up the table for my cousins, but then he announced that he had to leave. "I'll be back on my way to the train station, Doris. Do you think you could walk me to the station?"

"I'll ask my parents, but I don't see why not," I said. "Take care, Tommy. I'll see you later."

As he left, I felt a small portion of my heart leave with him. My comfort was that I'd see him before he boarded the train for Camp LeJeune.

Tommy returned around four o'clock with his travel bag, wearing his uniform. When he entered the house, Aunt Eleanor was the first to speak. "Is this your boy, Doris? He's a marine now, huh? He looks better in that uniform than you did, Carmine."

"Hey. When we get home, I'll put my uniform on for you and we can take a trip down memory lane. What do you say?" Uncle Carm countered.

"You old fool," Aunt Eleanor replied. Then turning to us, she said, "Come on in, kids, and have something to eat."

"No, thank you, Aunt Ella," Tommy said. "I'm on my way to the train station and came to say goodbye to Doris."

Turning to me, he asked, "Are you able to walk me to the train station?"

Daddy responded, "We'll both walk you to the station, son. That way I can walk Doris back home."

"I'll go with you," Uncle Carm added.

"I'll get my coat," I said.

Mom came from the kitchen with a bag and handed it to Tommy. "I knew you weren't going to eat dinner, but I made you a sandwich for the trip. Meatballs on a hard roll." Then she whispered as if telling a great secret, "And a crumb bun. Have a good trip, Tommy. We'll see you next week, Doris said."

"Yes, Mrs. Messina. I plan to come back each weekend if I can get liberty. And thank you."

Mom nodded. "Well, let us know."

"I'm ready," I said.

Tommy and I walked down South Clover Street toward Main Street and the train station, followed by my father and Uncle Carm. It was noticeably cooler than it had been, so I took Tommy by the arm and held my coat closed with my other hand. We arrived at the station just as the conductors were boarding Tommy's train.

"You'll remember to visit my mother this week, won't you, Doris?" Tommy asked.

"Of course. I promised, and I won't forget."

"Okay. Well, I'll see you next Friday night. Hopefully I'll get better rides next week. I'll miss you."

"I'll miss you too," I replied, suddenly fighting back tears.

He took me in his arms and kissed me. "I love you, Doris."

"I love you too, Tommy."

He boarded the train for North Carolina, and as it

pulled away from the station, I wiped the tears from my eyes and turned to my waiting father and uncle, glad that they had the foresight to prevent a lonely walk home.

When my father took my left arm, Uncle Carm took my right arm and said, "Isn't it better to have the two men who love you most walking with you instead of that skinny boy?"

I smiled. "Of course it is, Uncle Carm, without a doubt."

THIRTEEN
Meeting Tommy's Family

On Tuesday evening, a frigid north wind ushered in a strong Canadian cold front. Nevertheless, I was determined to keep my promise to Tommy despite the bitter weather. I donned my heavy wool coat and started on my way to 28 Jefferson Street to meet Tommy's mother.

When I arrived, I was uncertain which house belonged to Tommy's family. There was a number 26 on a beautiful house with a freshly painted white picket fence, but the house next to it looked decrepit, not at all what I'd expected for a contractor's home.

The stairs had split boards, and the handrail was broken and unstable. The roof hanging over the porch was missing numerous shingles, and the tar paper had been torn away by the wind, exposing the bare wood. The soffit was sagging, and water stains marred the bare plaster. The house had peeling paint everywhere—windowsills, door frames, and clapboards all badly needed scraping and painting. The glass in the front door was missing, and a primitive piece of plywood was in its place to insulate from the cold.

I walked farther along the sidewalk to the next house, but the number 30 proved that this wasn't Tommy's house either. So I scaled the stairs of the decaying house carefully and rang the doorbell, which, thankfully, was functional.

A few moments later, I heard footsteps approaching the door and a voice stating, "I'm coming."

Immediately, I had the urge to run. What if this was the wrong house? What if Tommy's mother didn't like me? A wave of nausea swept over me, and I was completely startled when the door opened and a woman in a floral print house dress with an apron stared at me sternly and said, "Yes?"

I stood silently for what seemed like an eternity, then finally found words. "Hi. I, um, I'm Doris. I'm, um, looking for Mrs. Serino."

A broad smile broke across her face. "Well, you found her. Come on in, honey. Tommy told me you would be coming." She stepped to the side and opened the door wide.

I entered the dimly lit foyer and removed my gloves, placing them in my pocket.

After closing the door, Mrs. Serino turned to me. "Come this way, honey. We'll go in the kitchen." She was not a tall woman but stout, and the dress she wore hung loosely over her frame and made her seem wider than she was. The apron divided her midsection, accenting her large breasts, which, indicated by her rounded shoulders, caused her no small discomfort. Her face was framed by wire-rimmed glasses through which I saw a pair of beautiful blue eyes. Her dowdy manner of dress caused her to look older than her forty-two years, yet her welcoming smile warmed me and caused my tension to subside.

I followed her toward the brightly lit kitchen and took off my coat, placing it neatly over a nearby chair. Sitting down at the table, I surveyed the kitchen and was stunned at the state of complete disorder. There were dishes, baking utensils, and cups covering every horizontal surface. Interspersed between them were grocery items—jars, cans, and bags of flour, sugar, and macaroni. On the table were several used plates and utensils awaiting their turn in the overcrowded sink. On the wall was a small shrine with a statue of Saint Teresa of Avila adorned with palms from past Easters as well as relics and votive candles long ago spent.

"Would you like a cup of coffee, Doris?" Mrs. Serino asked, drawing my attention back to our visit.

"Yes, please," I said.

"Do you want black coffee or brown coffee?" Many people distinguished American coffee from Italian coffee by the difference in their color, with Italian coffee being of a darker, richer quality.

"I think brown coffee, please," I replied.

She filled the coffee pot with water and coffee grounds and placed it on the stove. Then she removed a plate from the cupboard and filled it with homemade cookies. (This was my first experience with my future mother-in-law's cookies, and even today I can say with total honesty that I've never tasted better cookies anywhere.) The cookies were twisted like anise cookies and topped with icing that was firmer than cake frosting but softer than a candy coating, and the various colors gave the plate a festive appearance.

As she placed the cookies before me, I suddenly realized

that she had been talking the entire time my eyes were wandering about the kitchen. "You must have done something to him, because I never seen Tommy act like this with any girl before," she was saying. "Do you take cream and sugar in your coffee? Help yourself to some cookies. These are vanilla flavored. Sometimes I make them with anisette or lemon, but I felt like doing these with vanilla."

Mrs. Serino chattered on, seemingly thankful for my company. "My daughter got married last year and now both of my sons are in the marines, so I get to spend a lot of time working on new recipes. Here, let me show you my daughter's wedding picture." She left the room and returned with a large photograph of the family taken at her daughter's wedding. "This is my daughter, Dolores, and my son-in-law, Johnny Gallo. He's a good fellow, this Johnny."

She pointed to Tommy in the photograph and smiled. "Of course you know him. And this is my oldest son, Jerry." She looked adoringly at the family portrait before placing it on the table.

In the photo was someone else, a man I recognized from his visit to my house back in August to inform me of Tommy's departure to Camp LeJeune—Mr. Serino. But she never acknowledged him.

"You haven't tasted the cookies yet," Mrs. Serino said and placed a handful on a napkin in front of me.

For almost two hours we talked about growing up in Poughkeepsie, who we knew in common, cooking, and a variety of other subjects. Finally, I said, "Well, it's getting late, and I really should be going. Thank you so much, Mrs. Serino. I really enjoyed our visit." I sincerely meant it. She really had made me feel welcomed.

"Okay, honey. Now don't be a stranger. You come and

see me anytime. Maybe you can come with me when I go to the Pollacks' to play canasta. Would you like that?"

Mrs. Serino asked that in such an affable manner that I couldn't refuse. "Yes, I would. Thank you."

She helped me with my coat, and as I put on my gloves, she took a small paper bag and filled it with cookies, then handed it to me and said, "Give these to your mother from me."

"Oh, how thoughtful. Thank you, Mrs. Serino," I said appreciatively.

At the door she gave me a hug and sent me on my way.

It was even colder now that the sun had gone down, so I walked home as quickly as I could. When I entered the house, I removed my gloves and coat, placed the gloves in the coat pocket, and hung the coat in the closet.

"Is that you, Doris?" my mother called.

"Yes, Mom."

"How was your visit with Tommy's mother?"

I joined her in the kitchen. "It was really very pleasant, Ma. She sent some of her cookies with me to give to you." I handed her the bag.

She pulled a cookie from the bag and took a bite. "Oh my," she said. "This is wonderful. I've never tasted something like it before, but it's very good." My mother was a woman of few compliments, so I knew that these cookies had made an impression on her.

Hearing the conversation in the kitchen, my father left his paper in the parlor and joined us.

My mother offered the bag to him. "Here, Joe, try these."

My father took a purple frosted cookie and with one bite devoured the entire thing. "It's good," was all he said.

"What kind of cookies are these, Joe?"

"They're not Sicilian cookies, I know that much," Daddy responded. This implied that while they may have been delicious cookies, they were not necessarily up to Sicilian standards.

"Oh, go back to your paper, will you," Mom reprimanded.

My dad took another cookie, ate it, and left the room.

"So how was Tommy's mother? Was she nice to you?" Now she sounded a little concerned.

"She was very pleasant. We talked a lot about Poughkeepsie. Her parents came right here from Apice, Benevento, in Italy. Her grandmother owned a grocery store in Mount Carmel Square, and she was the one who taught her how to cook. Her mother died when she was born, so she never knew her. She showed me photos of her family—her daughter and son-in-law and her sons, but she didn't talk at all about her husband. I thought that was rather strange."

My mother nodded. "He's a contractor, I believe. They must have a nice house."

"Actually, quite the opposite. The house is much more rundown than I expected. I almost passed it by completely. Mrs. Serino is certainly a good baker, but she's not much of a housekeeper."

"Well, there are always reasons behind actions," was all my mother said before she changed the subject. "Are you hungry, Doris? I made lentil soup tonight. I'll warm some up for you."

"Oh yes, thanks. It's so cold outside. Soup is just what I need to warm me inside."

As I ate the steaming bowl of lentils, I reflected on the success of the day and realized that I would have many

things to share with Tommy in the letter I'd write to him
that night.

~

When the weekend came, Tommy was again able to obtain
liberty. So Friday night was another sleepless night in anticipation of his arrival. It was colder now, so the windows
were closed. About one in the morning, I thought that I
heard something hit my window. I lay quietly, hoping it
wasn't a bat or some other night creature trying to enter
through the glass. Then I heard it again, louder this time.

That's when Kay awoke and said, "Oh, for goodness'
sake, Doris, will you open that window and tell Tommy to
stop throwing rocks. He's going to break the glass."

I jumped from the bed and opened the window just in
time to stop Tommy from throwing a third pebble.
"Tommy, you're back. I'll open the door." I put on my
housecoat and rushed down the stairs.

But to my surprise Daddy was already there and
opened the door to a very surprised Tommy. "Welcome
back, son. Come on in out of the cold."

I hugged Tommy around the neck, and he kissed me
and shook my father's hand. "Thank you, sir." Turning to
me, he asked, "How are you, Doris?"

"Let's go upstairs before we wake the neighborhood,"
Dad said.

We were soon settled in the kitchen, and I said to
Tommy, "You got back earlier this week."

"I had much better luck with rides. I think it might be due
to the cold weather. Down South, I never have any trouble
getting a ride. They see the uniform and I often get rides as far

north as Delaware, Maryland, or New Jersey. But up North, rides are harder to find. I noticed that since the weather has turned colder, people are more willing to offer rides."

"Do you want some coffee, Tommy?" my father asked.

"Yes, sir. That would be nice."

Daddy put on the coffee and went into the parlor to allow us a little privacy.

"I went to see your mother this week, Tommy," I told him. "We had a very nice visit. She was really sweet to me."

"You caught her on a good day, then. And you obviously saw my house. Now you know why I never wanted to take you there. I've always been embarrassed by the condition both inside and out." He spoke candidly about subjects he would never speak of before. "My dad does nothing to fix the house, and my mother... well, you've seen her idea of housekeeping. She's always out. She comes home to cook and that's it. I could never bear to see the shock on your face when you first saw my house, so I never took you there. But now that you have been there, I want you to meet the rest of my family."

"I'd like that, Tommy," I said.

My dad came back in to serve the coffee, then sat with us for a short time until Tommy had to leave. We all knew he would be back bright and early in the morning and that the opportunity for sleep was quickly passing.

The next morning, Tommy arrived just as we were finishing breakfast. He had coffee and a hard roll with us, so my mother was pleased that he ate something. While I finished my chores, Tommy and Daddy went into the parlor and talked about Tommy's future in the military. I wasn't able to hear what they were talking about, but Tommy told me later.

"Now that basic training is finished, I'll be starting radio school on Monday," he explained. "I'll be training as a radio operator, learning both the procedure and language of communication in the field."

"And where will you use this new knowledge?" my dad asked, obviously having a more serious question in mind.

"Well, sir, our unit will be going to Korea. There's a conflict there between the North and South, and President Truman has ordered troops moved in as a peacekeeping force."

"I see. Will you be going into combat, then?"

"Not definitively, sir. We're being sent to Korea, but how close we'll be to combat is uncertain right now."

Daddy nodded. "Let's just hope that for your sake, and Doris's, that you won't be close at all." After a few moments of silence, he went on. "And what about when your military service is finished? What will you do then?"

"I don't know for certain, but I believe I'll apprentice with my father as a bricklayer. I prefer outside work to factory work." Tommy then seemed to realize what he'd said. "No offense intended, sir."

Daddy laughed. "I prefer a lot of things to factory work myself."

When I finished my chores, Tommy and I prepared to leave.

"Where are you going today?" my mother called from the kitchen.

"To my house, Mrs. Messina. My sister and her husband are coming over to meet Doris."

This was news to me, and a new wave of anxiousness swept over me.

"Later we'll be going to the movies," Tommy continued.

Satisfied with our itinerary, Mom said, "Okay, have fun. And thank your mother for the cookies she sent over."

When we reached Tommy's house, his sister and brother-in-law had already arrived.

"Where have you been, little brother?" she teased him. "I've been here for an hour waiting for you to bring this pretty girl over. Is this her? Hi, I'm Dolores. I'm the big sister to this bum." She pointed to Tommy. "And this is my husband, Johnny."

John Gallo was a handsome man with a calm and kind spirit. He was a carpenter, and his hands were hard and calloused from manual labor, but his grip was warm and gentle. He shook my hand and said, "I'm glad to know you." I liked him immediately.

Dolores was a firecracker. I would come to know her as a take-charge woman, highly capable of managing multiple tasks simultaneously. She worked as a telephone operator, an occupation that employed this special talent regularly. She was a motivator, always on high intensity, so she and Johnny were, in my opinion, perfectly matched, for when Dolores would become too high strung, Johnny's undisturbed demeanor had a calming effect. And when Johnny's laid-back personality would cause hesitation, his wife's "motivator gifting" would give him the inspiration needed to make the necessary move.

Dolores and I were friends from that day forward. Many weekends when Tommy would come home, we would visit Dolores and Johnny in their home on Gifford Avenue. I truly enjoyed getting to know them and spending time with them.

Now, Dolores called out, "Ma, did you put the coffee on yet?"

"No, I didn't!" Mrs. Serino shot back sharply.

Dolores turned to me. "She's in a mood today. You'll get used to it." She then went to the kitchen to fix the coffee.

Tommy, Johnny, and I sat down in the parlor, and Johnny asked me, "So, Doris, are you from Poughkeepsie?"

"Well, I was born in New Windsor, but I've lived in Poughkeepsie since I was eight years old."

"Are you still in school?"

"No, I work at the pocketbook factory on Canon Street where my dad works."

"Oh, I know people who work there. Who's your dad?" Johnny asked.

"Joe Messina."

He squinted. "I don't think I know him. Messina? Are you Sicilian?"

"Half," I giggled. "My mother is Scots-Irish."

"My mother and father are both from Sicily." He then turned to Tommy. "How's basic training going for you, old man?"

"Thankfully I'm through with basic. I'll be starting radio school on Monday," Tommy answered. "Then my unit is supposed to be shipped out for Korea."

This came as a shock to me. I hadn't heard this bit of information before, and I was certain I didn't like it.

"Coffee's ready!" Dolores called from the kitchen.

We all rose and proceeded to the kitchen, where Dolores had set the table with cups, saucers, plates, and a tray full of Rosette cookies, Tommy's favorite. Mrs. Serino was at the sink washing breakfast dishes.

"Come on, Ma," Dolores said to her. "Come and have some coffee."

"I'm busy right now. Can't you see that?" Mrs. Serino snapped back.

Dolores turned to us and whispered, "I told you she's in a mood."

The afternoon was enjoyable, with Tommy and his sister bantering back and forth. Mrs. Serino began to brighten a little, though never completely leaving her ill humor. Johnny and I sat back and enjoyed the antics of the Serino siblings from our front-row seats.

Soon it was time for Dolores and Johnny to leave. "Come on over to visit anytime," she told me at the door. "You don't need to bring this palooka. I really enjoyed getting to know you, Doris." Then turning to her brother, she said, "Take good care of yourself, little brother. Hopefully I'll see you soon."

"I will, Dolores. I love you." Tommy kissed her on the cheek and then pulled off her earring and handed it to her.

"Tommy, you bastard!" Dolores cringed. "Now you made me cuss in front of this nice girl."

"She'll get used to it, being around you," Johnny said to his wife.

"Don't listen to them, Doris," she protested. "I'm the nice one in the family."

"Come on, Dolores," Johnny said. "Let's get home. Your nose is growing already."

Once they were gone, Tommy turned to me. "My sister is a character, isn't she?"

"And you tease her mercilessly," I responded in Dolores's defense.

"Ouch! I guess I see whose side you're on," Tommy conceded.

We went back into the kitchen, where Tommy told his mother, "We need to be going too, Ma. We have a movie to catch."

"Fine," Mrs. Serino replied.

"I'm leaving tomorrow on the five o'clock train. I want to come and say goodbye to you. Will you be home?"

"I don't know. I might be at Little Mary's house."

"Okay. We'll see you, Ma," Tommy said and turned to leave.

"What—no kiss for your mother?" she snapped at him.

He obediently went and kissed his mother on the cheek. "Bye, Ma."

"Goodbye," was her curt response.

We left, and on the way back to my house Tommy seemed somewhat disconsolate. I broke the silence by saying, "I really enjoyed being with your sister and her husband. They seem like a fun couple to be around. They remind me of Uncle Carm and Aunt Eleanor."

Tommy ignored my words. "Did you see how surly my mother was? That's how she usually is. When she gets in her moods, she wants everyone to cater to her. My sister and I won't do it anymore."

"Everyone has days when they don't feel happy" I said, trying to smooth the situation.

"Everyone has days, but she's had a lifetime of it."

We walked in silence the rest of the way to my house.

I began to visit Tommy's family with some consistency. I went with Mrs. Serino to play cards with her friends, the Pollacks. They were wonderful people and took me in as one of their own. Mrs. Serino was often difficult to please, though. It seemed that nothing ever satisfied her, and her mood would frequently turn sour. She was, as everyone knew, an excellent cook, and I was hoping to learn from her, but she was stingy with her recipes and would share very little of her techniques.

Nevertheless, I spent as much time with her as I could. When Tommy would come home on the weekends, we would often visit Dolores and Johnny. I really enjoyed their company, and time spent with them was never dull. Dolores and I got along well, and Tommy was always teasing Johnny or attempting to stir Dolores into a frenzy.

One weekend when Tommy was able to get liberty, we went to visit his mother. Upon walking into the kitchen, I was surprised to see Mr. Serino sitting at the table. Mrs. Serino was preparing something on the stove, and a heavenly aroma filled the air.

"Hi, Ma. Hi, Pop," Tommy said.

Mrs. Serino didn't acknowledge his greeting, but when Mr. Serino saw me, he rose from his chair to greet me, "Hello, Doris. How are you, honey?"

"I'm fine. Mr. Serino. It's nice to see you again."

"You've met my dad?" Tommy asked, obviously surprised.

"He came to my house to tell me you'd joined the marines," I explained. "I'll never forget that thoughtful and compassionate gesture."

"Come and sit," Mr. Serino said. "How have you been, Doris? What are you doing when Tommy's no here?"

"Well, I work at Goldcrest Fashions, the pocketbook factory on Canon Street, during the day. And Mrs. Serino has been keeping me busy introducing me to various friends," I said, trying to draw Tommy's mom into the conversation.

"Has she met Jerry yet?" he asked Tommy.

"Not yet, Pop. That's why I brought her here today."

Turning toward the parlor, Mr. Serino called out, "Jerry! Come in here. There's somebody you got to meet."

Abruptly, Mrs. Serino turned and said, "Germano, do you want more sausage before I put it away?"

"No, no," was his equally brusque response. The perceptible tension between them chilled the room like an arctic breeze.

Tommy's brother entered the kitchen, lessening the anxiety I was feeling. He was dressed in a marine uniform and approached me with a welcoming grin, saying, "You must be Doris. I'm so pleased to meet you."

Jerry was an attractive man with a swarthy complexion and a beautiful smile. He and Tommy looked very much alike, falling two or three degrees short of identical twins. Unlike Kay and I who, although we're sisters, bear very little resemblance, they were obviously brothers. I would soon learn that, in addition to his appealing countenance, Jerry's most attractive quality was his personality. He was charming and funny, and I liked him immediately.

"I'm glad to make your acquaintance, Jerry. I see that you're in the marines also."

He nodded. "I was in the navy during the war and just recently enlisted in the marines."

"A much better choice," Tommy interjected. "He went from a squid to a man."

"Just keep your shirt on over that bare chest, little brother," Jerry laughed. "We're both stationed at Camp LeJeune right now, and it's just a coincidence that we both have liberty at the same time."

I turned to Mrs. Serino, still busy at the stove, and said,

"It must be nice to have both sons home at the same time, Mrs. Serino."

"Well, Tommy comes home all the time, but it's nice to have Jerry here," she replied.

A hurt look crossed Tommy's face, and I quickly changed the subject. "You must be proud of both of your boys, Mr. Serino."

"Yes, yes, they good boys," he answered, looking proudly from one to the other. Then he addressed his wife. "Sophie, did you make coffee?"

"No, Germano, I've been busy," she countered.

"I'll make the coffee, Ma," Jerry said.

After having a cup of coffee and spending some time with his sons, Mr. Serino rose from the table. "I have to go and check on a job. It was nice to see you again, Doris. I hope to see more of you. Bye, honey." After kissing me on the cheek, he kissed both of his sons and called to his wife, who'd left the room, "Sophie, I'll be back later!"

There was no response, so he exited the kitchen and left.

When the front door closed, Mrs. Serino returned to the kitchen. "I don't know what he expects from me."

"Not now, Ma," Tommy said.

Jerry added, "We'll talk about it later, Ma. We have a guest right now."

Mrs. Serino turned to me. "I'm sorry, Doris. That man infuriates me." Then she looked around at all of us. "Does anyone want more coffee?"

"No, Ma. Doris and I have to go anyway," Tommy said. "I promised Dolores we'd stop by before we go to the movies tonight. I'll be home later."

"Okay," Mrs. Serino answered more calmly this time. "Bye, Doris. Are you coming on Tuesday to play cards?"

"Yes, ma'am." I really enjoyed playing canasta with her and her friends.

"Okay, then. I'll see you Tuesday." She turned her attention to Tommy and said tersely, "Am I going to see you before you go this time?"

"Are you going to be home?" Tommy countered.

"I don't know. Just look for me," she said.

Tommy kissed her, said a quick goodbye to his brother, and headed for the front door.

"Bye-bye, Doe," Jerry said to me. "It was nice to meet you. My kid brother is a lucky son of a gun." He gave me a fraternal kiss on the cheek. "I hope to see you soon."

"Bye, Jerry. It was nice to meet you too. Bye, Mrs. Serino."

"Goodbye, honey," she replied. "See you next week."

I joined Tommy at the front door and kissed his cheek.

"What was that for?" he asked.

"Just because I love you."

"And don't forget it," he responded with a smile.

Tommy was able to get liberty almost every weekend through the remainder of the year. We spent every possible moment together. I met other members of Tommy's family, including his mother's sister, Aunt Tessie, and her husband, Uncle Mike, his mother's brother, Uncle Phil, and we even took a bus ride to Beacon to visit his father's brother Uncle Tony and his wife, Aunt Anna.

When the holidays arrived, Tommy spent Thanksgiving and Christmas with my family, which made my mother very happy. The new year was approaching, and we looked forward to closing the chapter on 1949 and the decade of war. Everyone had high hopes for the prospects of the coming year. Tommy and I were together, and our future was becoming clearer.

But life's circumstances observe no boundaries or limitations, and the unpredictable events we experience often result in unanticipated adjustments. New Year's Eve 1950 promised so much that we never anticipated how, before the end of the year, we would experience events that would bring life-changing consequences.

FOURTEEN
The Accident

Tommy had gotten his orders. His unit was being deployed to Korea by the end of May. There was an air of excitement among the men. They were a unit, a team, and together they were going overseas to make a difference in the world. Many briefings were held, instructing the units on the nature of the war, the ideological conflict between the North and the South, the climate of Korea, and other aspects of life in the time of war on this small Asiatic peninsula. The men prepared and packed, and all their necessary belongings were loaded onto the ship.

On May 13, 1950, an officer approached Tommy and three others from his unit. "Men," the officer ordered, "get over to that ship on the far side of the dock and assist them in unloading. When you're finished, you'll have liberty until lights-out. Understand?"

"Yes sir," was the response from four men, and they hustled over to the dock where the unloading of the large ship was underway.

A massive derrick was employed to perform the task. Cargo was loaded on pallets, and chains were attached to the four corners of each platform. The chains were joined together by a large metal ring that was subsequently attached to a hook supported by the crane. When the hoist would turn, the chains would pull taut, lifting the entire pallet of freight. The pallets were raised precipitously, often causing the contents to shift, while the men stood below as the crane lowered the pallet to the dock. It was then unloaded, and its contents dispersed to their final destination.

As the men waited for yet another pallet of freight to descend, Tommy noticed that this load had shifted considerably, causing one crate to move dangerously close to the edge of the platform. As the derrick swung away from the ship, the pallet twisted and the container slipped from it and plunged toward the dock. One man was standing directly under the load of freight and didn't see the container fall.

Tommy reacted instinctively, shouting, "Watch out!" and running toward the man. He pushed him away in time, but Tommy wasn't so fortunate. As he pushed the man, Tommy twisted to avoid being struck by the box, but the crate struck him just above his left knee. As Tommy and the other man lay on the dock, stunned and uncertain of what had happened, the other men hurried to drag them away in case any other cargo dislodged and fell.

Tommy's leg was bleeding through his torn trousers, and the marines began to assess the situation. "Can you stand?" a marine asked Tommy.

"I think so," Tommy replied, and two men assisted him to his feet. Putting pressure on his leg, Tommy was relieved to find there was no pain, indicating no broken bones or torn tendons. "I think it's just a cut," he assured them. "I just need a bandage. I'll be fine."

"I think you should report to sick bay," one of the men cautioned him. "You may need stitches or something. Get it checked out."

But Tommy refused. "I'm fine. We're shipping out, and I don't want anything to hold me back."

"Okay, then," one of the marines agreed. "Let's get you back to the barracks and bandage that leg. We've got a few more pallets to unload."

Tommy, accompanied by another marine, returned to the barracks and bandaged the leg after observing that the cut was in reality a four-inch gash and quite deep. Tommy was determined to be on the ship with his unit, though, so he steadfastly refused to go to sick bay, insisting that the wound was superficial. By the time they returned to the dock, the other men had unloaded the ship and they were free to enjoy the remainder of the day.

The men went to the mess hall, and after having lunch they were ready to enjoy their liberty. Tommy wanted to go into town to purchase a gift to send to Doris as a promise of his safe return.

As he exited the mess hall with the other men, two officers approached. "Where are the men involved in the unloading incident this morning?"

"Here, sir," Tommy and the other man responded.

"Which one of you sustained an injury?" the officer inquired.

"It was me, sir," Tommy replied, "but it's just a small cut. I have it bandaged and it's fine."

"If you say so, Marine," the officer said. "Just don't leave base, and report to me later this afternoon."

Tommy was disappointed but returned to the barracks to write his daily correspondence to Doris.

Several hours later, one of his buddies entered the barracks and told Tommy he needed to report to headquarters. When he stood, there was a tenderness around the wound and pressure that he hadn't felt before. The short jaunt across the base to headquarters proved more painful than anticipated, and when he arrived, Tommy had a slight limp. Approaching the officer's desk, Tommy announced, "Pfc. Serino reporting, sir."

Without looking up, the officer said, "Serino, report to the dispensary on the double."

"Begging your pardon, sir, I don't need to go to sick bay," Tommy protested. "I'm fine. It's just a small cut."

"I'm not interested in your assessment of the injury, Private. I want a medical opinion. Are you a doctor?"

"No, sir. But I would rather not be tied up in sick bay, sir. My unit is leaving for Korea and—"

"I'm not interested in your affairs, Private," the officer interrupted. "Write to Dear Abby if you have concerns. Right now, report to sick bay. That's an order."

"And if I refuse, sir?"

"You'll be court-martialed, Private, and you'll sit in jail guarded by MPs while your unit goes to Korea. Make your choice, Marine."

Knowing he had no other choice, Tommy conceded, "Private Serino reporting to sick bay, sir."

At the dispensary, the doctors removed the bandage on Tommy's leg to reveal a gash that had widened due to swelling and was beginning to exude a pinkish substance. They immediately aspirated his leg, removing approximately 30 to 40 cc of fluid. They wrapped his leg tightly and told him to remain seated on the examination table until they returned.

About ten minutes later, the doctor returned with a signed order for Tommy to report to sick bay immediately after roll call the next morning for a recheck on the wound. The next day Tommy arrived at the dispensary as ordered, and the doctor removed the bandage to reveal the wound swollen like it had been the previous day. The doctor again aspirated 30 to 40 cc of pink fluid, then released Tommy to duty with an order to return the next morning at the same time.

This process continued for nine days. Finally, the doctor said, "Private Serino, your injury is such that we're not able to effectively treat it here."

"What does that mean, sir?" Tommy inquired.

"You have trauma to the suprapatellar and peripatellar region on the left quadricep area as a result of the crate striking your leg. We've aspirated each day, but the swelling continues unabated. I understand that your unit was to go on maneuvers, but your knee is not improving and you're not physically able to accompany them."

"But sir, the leg really isn't a problem," Tommy insisted. "I'm certain the swelling will subside soon."

The doctor shook his head. "We're making arrangements for the ambulance to transport you to Quantico, Virginia. You will be admitted to the naval hospital there for treatment."

"But I can't go to Virginia, Doctor. My unit is shipping out soon."

"You are being shipped out today, Marine," the doctor replied pragmatically. "We'll send your belongings after you."

"I don't have any belongings," Tommy told him. "They're all loaded aboard ship for Korea."

"This is the marines, son. We'll replace your belongings. Besides, you won't be needing them for a while."

Crushing disappointment overwhelmed Tommy. He fell silent and turned toward the wall to await the arrival of the ambulance.

At the naval hospital, Tommy was given a complete examination. Two doctors were present, and they pushed and prodded his thighs while twisting and turning his leg in every imaginable direction. He carried with him the following report from the dispensary at Camp LeJeune.

Hemorrhage. Traumatic, NEC (Left knee – peripatellar)
1. Within command.
2. Work.
3. Negligence not apparent.
4. Packing case fell on left leg.

Examination reveals fluctuant, non-tender swelling just above the left knee in the area of the supra-patella pouch. There is a crusted abrasion about 6 c. prox. to the patella. There is increased local heat but no erythema. Little pain on motion of the knee joint. No femoral lymphadenopathy. This area has been aspirated daily since injury sustained at the post dispensary. From 30-40 cc of pink to bloody fluid have been removed each time, however, swelling continues to recur.

5-23-50: To USNH, Quantico, Virginia for treatment and disposition.

A. A. Cairo
LTJG MC USNR

Tommy was admitted and given a private hospital

room. Although it was comfortable and accommodating, to Tommy it felt like a prison cell. Before he could settle in his temporary barracks, a nurse arrived to take him to x-ray. Afterward he was returned to his room, given some lunch, and left to await the doctor's prognosis.

Several hours later, two doctors entered his room. "Private Serino? I'm Captain Robbin, the lead physician assigned to your case, and this is Lieutenant Canamucio. He will be your attending physician. How is the leg feeling presently, Private?"

"I don't have any pain at all, sir," Tommy answered optimistically.

"Glad to hear it. Private, as you know there is a fluctuant, non-tender swelling just above the left knee, but there appears to be little to no pain on motion of the knee joint. The problem is the continuous buildup of fluid and the indication of infection. We are treating the infection with penicillin, but so far, the leg does not seem to be responding. Our concern is that if we cannot control the swelling, then amputation becomes a very real possibility."

Tommy stared at him. "You want to cut my leg off? It was just a cut on the knee."

"Relax, Private, that would only be considered as a last resort," the doctor assured him. "The treatment we're proposing is a posterior plaster splint applied from the gluteal fold to the ankle with a ten-degree flexion of the knee. In other words, you'll have a cast from your ass to your ankle. This, along with bed rest, elevating the left leg, daily whirlpool baths, and a continued regimen of penicillin to treat the infection, should take the swelling down. Do you understand?"

"Yes, sir."

"Very good, then. Cooperate with your treatment and you should be out of here in a few weeks," the captain said.

"Sir? When can I get leave to see my girl?"

"Is she local, Private?" the captain asked.

"No, sir. She's in New York."

"Not until you're mobile, then."

The two medical officers left Tommy alone with his sobering prognosis. He was not about to lose his leg, so he would do everything necessary to ensure that didn't happen.

Tommy wrote to tell me that he wouldn't be coming home that weekend, but he said nothing of the incident or of his hospitalization. I did notice the address change, but I knew that Tommy was to be shipping out to Korea, so I assumed it was the port of departure.

The doctors continued to monitor Tommy's progress. The full leg cast had a positive effect on the swelling, and by June 6, Tommy was on crutches. He had written to me and explained that he had cut his leg and was in the hospital in a cast. But he assured me that it was a minor injury and he would be able to visit soon. Tommy was in the hospital for almost three weeks when he received his first liberty.

Tommy said nothing to anyone about his condition. He acquired liberty from the hospital almost every weekend during his recovery, and amazingly, he would hitchhike from Quantico, Virginia, to Poughkeepsie, New York, as he had prior to the accident. Even when he wore the cast from his hip to his toes, he was undeterred and hitchhiked back to Poughkeepsie every weekend possible.

He arrived in the middle of the night, as he had on previous visits. When I opened the door to let him in, he had hidden the crutches to the side obscured by the open door, but I immediately noticed the cast on his left leg.

"Tommy! Oh my, did you come all this way in a cast?" I asked, unable to hide the concern in my voice.

"Oh, it's nothing, really," he said. "Gee, it's good to see you again, Doris. I'll see you tomorrow morning, okay?"

"Okay." I was a little surprised that he didn't stay longer, but he had to be tired after his long journey. I peeked through the window and watched him descend the stairs, then take the crutches from their resting place behind the door and carefully use them for support, leading each time with his right leg and holding on to the railing. It seemed that his injury was more severe than he was admitting, but I would have to wait until tomorrow to find out.

The following morning when Tommy arrived, I was prepared with my inquest. He appeared promptly at eight o'clock with a big smile and small gift for me. As we walked up to the apartment, I paid close attention to how he ascended the stairs. He seemed to approach them less cautiously than last night, maneuvering the crutches with expertise. We entered the kitchen, and Tommy sat down at the table.

"Good morning, Tommy," my mother said. "Can I get you some breakfast?"

"Just coffee, please, Mrs. Messina," Tommy replied.

My mother placed a cup in front of him, along with a basket of hard rolls and a plate of bacon strategically positioned in the center of the table but close enough to Tommy for easy access. She also placed some rhubarb on the table, having picked some earlier in the year and boiled it until tender and then sweetened it with sugar.

I sat next to Tommy and opened the box he had given me. Inside was a kewpie doll wearing a little diaper with "I love you" embroidered on it. "Awww, it's so cute," I said. "Thanks." I kissed him on the cheek.

Tommy blushed slightly. "I saw him in the gift shop at the hospital before I left and knew I had to get him for you."

Before he realized what he'd said, I gasped. "You're still in the hospital?"

This brought the attention of the entire family, and he became visibly uncomfortable. "Well, yes, but it really isn't a big deal. I cut my leg on a box about three weeks ago and wasn't able to ship out with my unit."

"Thank God," my mother whispered as she turned to fill my father's coffee cup. "Joe, breakfast is ready!"

My father was already coming in from the parlor, and having heard the mention of a continued hospitalization, his interest was piqued.

Tommy continued with his vague recounting of the incident. "Like I was saying, I cut my leg on a crate and, I don't know, I guess it got a little infected, so they wouldn't let me board ship. They sent me to sick bay and transferred me to the naval hospital at Quantico, Virginia."

"Are you out of the hospital now?" I asked.

"Not yet. They're still giving me medicine and draining my leg. It keeps swelling." Tommy was clearly being evasive with his answers.

My father was much more direct in his approach. "How did you cut your leg, Tommy? It must be a severe cut. After all, they don't put you in the hospital for minor lacerations."

Tommy straightened and thought for a moment. "Well, sir, the cut was a little deeper than I first thought. But the problem is that it keeps swelling. They've been draining it every day, but it continues to fill with fluid." Tommy shrugged. "I was told that as soon as the swelling is under control, I'll be released from the hospital. In the meantime, I can get liberty every weekend, with the doctor's consent.

They want me to pursue normal activity on the weekends so they can monitor the results on Monday."

"Are you in pain, Tommy?" I asked, no longer able to hide my uneasiness.

"Not really. Only when they drain the fluid."

I didn't really believe him. Tommy was trying to put on a brave face and minimize the extent of the injury. I knew that if there was no cause for concern, they wouldn't keep him in the hospital. Also, a knee doesn't build up that much fluid daily unless something is very wrong.

"Well, I'm sure you're disappointed to be separated from your unit, but frankly I'm glad you won't be going into combat," Dad said. "I think you had someone watching over you in this incident." Daddy had no idea how prophetic his words were.

Tommy spent half of 1950 in the hospital at Quantico. The long cast from hip to ankle gave limited success. By the middle of June, the hematoma was absorbing and the abrasion healing. Unfortunately, by the end of June, Tommy was still having joint effusion and attempts to aspirate the knee proved unsuccessful. This resulted in the application of a second cast from the upper thigh to the lower leg. Tommy wore this "short cast," as he called it, until the end of July.

The doctors continued to fight the swelling, and by the end of August they were winning the battle. Tommy was released from the hospital on September 6 and returned to active duty, but he was declared unfit for combat. The incision was considered healed and the recommendation of continued physiotherapy to the left leg was advised because the doctors told him that he could eventually lose his leg.

Thankfully this never occurred, although as he grew older the leg caused him no small amount of pain. His unit shipped out without him, along with all his belongings that he never recovered. A new radio man was assigned to the unit in Tommy's place, and while in Korea his unit came under fire and the radio man was killed by a sniper's bullet, shot through the radio.

Tommy had saved a man's life on the dock at Camp LeJeune, and another man was killed in Tommy's place in Korea.

FIFTEEN

Year of Change

The year 1950 would be a year of many changes for my family. We purchased our first refrigerator in the spring. No more emptying the drip tray or worrying about the floorboards. And we were now able to purchase food for more than two days. The refrigerator was about as tall as me, although I couldn't look over the top. Inside it had adjustable shelves and even shelving on the door. There was a drawer to keep vegetables, which my mother called a crisper, and it even had a small freezing area that came with trays for making ice cubes. I believed it to be the most marvelous machine I had ever seen.

Daddy also bought his first automobile in the spring of 1950. It was a Kaiser Fraser, a beautiful car. Up until this time few cars were on the road. Most people walked where they needed to go. Long-distance trips, such as visiting the family in New Windsor, required a bus ride. The bus would pick us up in Union Square and take us to Beacon, and from Beacon we would take the ferry across the river to Newburgh. There Uncle Morgan would pick us up in his truck or we would walk the two miles to New Windsor. But now we would be able to drive from our house directly to our destination. I felt so rich because of this privilege.

In the latter part of the year, we bought our first television. Televisions, or TVs as most people called them, became available to the public in 1949. They were very expensive, with an average cost between two and three hundred dollars, or approximately four to five weeks' salary for a factory worker.

My mother was very proud of her television. It was a large wooden box with a little round ten-inch screen in the middle. It required an antenna to be installed on the roof and would often have poor reception if the weather was bad or the wind was blowing, or sometimes for no reason at all. It was possible to get better reception if an additional, smaller antenna was installed and placed on the top of the television. These antennae were called "rabbit ears" because they mimicked the natural ears of a rabbit—long, vertical, and able to turn in various directions to receive signals.

When the television was turned on, it took several minutes for the tubes inside to warm up, and the picture would gradually take form and become progressively clearer. Likewise, when the television was turned off, the screen would immediately go black, apart from a small white dot in the center of the picture tube. The hypnotic effect of the dot caused the entire family to sit perfectly still, completely mesmerized, staring at the dot until it disappeared. The programs were all in black and white, and we would often try to guess the color of objects on the screen from their shade of gray.

In late spring, I quit my job at the factory and began work at Vassar Hospital in the kitchen. My job was to clean and prep the doctors' dining area. They had a reserved, strictly monitored section of the cafeteria that was separated from the area for the general populace. The doctors appreciated having a private area, and I thought they were just haughty, thinking themselves better than others. I certainly didn't understand their need for a sanctuary.

Once the doctor's dining room was clean and respectable, I was to supervise the coffee in the main cafeteria. I had to make the coffee, keep the service area clean, and, at the end of the day, thoroughly clean the coffee machines. That was the part I despised the most. I had to stand on an unstable stool and bend over the large canisters to reach the bottom. More than once I felt the pedestal shift beneath my feet, causing me to grasp the coffee maker for support.

The best part of the job was the walk to work each morning with Tommy's Uncle Mike.

He was the kindest, gentlest man I had ever met, and was married to Aunt Tessie, Tommy's mother's sister. They lived on Jefferson Street across from Tommy's family and above a grocery store. Aunt Tessie was a lovely person, humorous and personable. She was friends with everyone and always had company, so the coffee pot was always percolating in their house. Uncle Mike was a quiet man, much in contrast to his wife, who was always the prankster. Whenever Aunt Tessie was together with her brother, Uncle Phil, the antics between the two of them kept the comedy going for hours. Through all this, Uncle Mike would sit back with a smile on his face and quietly enjoy the chaos. Aunt Tessie and Uncle Mike became good friends with my parents, and they would visit each other frequently.

Uncle Mike was a janitor at Vassar Hospital, so each morning he would wait for me to walk over from my house to Jefferson Street, then we would walk the remainder of the way together. As we walked, Uncle Mike would tell me stories about Tommy, about his and Aunt Tessie's children, about growing up in Italy, and about anything that would come to mind. I think he enjoyed being able to talk freely without being interrupted by his exuberant wife.

Years later when Tommy and I owned our house in Red Oaks Mill, Uncle Mike would come to the house and work in the yard all day. He loved the outdoors and watching things grow. The last thing he planted before his death was a small maple tree on the east side of the front yard. The tree was just a twig when he planted it, but today it stands over fifty feet tall. Uncle Mike was my companion, my guardian, and my favorite.

With the coming of warmer weather, we were able to leave our bedroom windows open at night. I became so accustomed to Tommy arriving on Friday nights that I could recognize his walk as he approached. We spent a great deal of time together visiting our families, going to the movies, and talking about our future.

In the spring of 1950, Tommy approached my father with an important question. It was Saturday morning, and he came to the house bright and early as usual. Then after breakfast he asked my father if he could speak to him in private. Mom, Kay, and I remained in the kitchen while the men retreated to the parlor.

There, they sat across from each other and got comfortable. Each one knew that there could be no distractions to the serious tone of the imminent conversation. Daddy was the first to speak. "Well, son, what's on your mind?"

"Mr. Messina, I would like to marry your daughter," Tommy said in his direct, to-the-point manner.

Daddy paused. "I see. But you're in the service right now. Would it be a practical time to marry?" He was a wise man, ever realistic in his considerations, and he certainly could remember how difficult it was for he and my mother when they were first married. He wanted to avoid his daughters having unnecessary complications in their newlywed experience.

"Well, sir," Tommy responded, "I've been in almost a year, and I'll be going overseas. But I love Doris and want to make a life for us together."

"And how do you propose to do that? How are you planning to make a life for you and Doris?" Daddy countered.

"I'd originally considered making a career in the military, possibly requesting an assignment in Australia. But Doris is very close to you all and taking her away from here would be devastating to her. So, I've decided to finish my tour of duty and then apprentice with my father as a bricklayer, then join the bricklayer's union. I can make a good living as a mason and support Doris adequately."

Daddy nodded, seeing that Tommy wasn't presumptuous regarding his future and had a plan that put my needs above his own opportunity to see the world.

"I would like to marry your daughter and spend my life with her," Tommy continued. "I love her, and I will always take care of her."

After several moments of thought, Daddy finally spoke. "You have my blessing but promise me you won't get married until you get out of the service."

"We won't, Mr. Messina. Thank you."

Not much changed after that. Tommy continued to

come home every weekend. The news of our impending marriage spread among our friends and family members, and as in every Italian family, each person had an opinion that they were quick to share with whomever was within audible range. We talked constantly about our future, and by August Tommy was pressing ever harder about getting married. His consistent plea was, "We need to get married."

This was sooner than my father preferred, so I spoke with my mother and expressed my desire to be Tommy's wife. Her words were few but meaningful. "Your father told you that you should wait until Tommy is finished in the service," she reminded me. "Tommy agreed. Now you come back and say that you don't want to wait, that you want to marry now."

"Yes, Mom, we do. I love Tommy and he loves me."

"Marriage is more than the affection you feel today, Doris," she told me.

Now I was upset. "We truly love each other, Ma. Don't you know what love is?" As a hurt look crossed my mother's face, I immediately regretted my outburst.

"I have lived with your father for twenty years, and we have been through hell together. Despite all of it we have remained committed to each other. Do you have that kind of love, Doris? Do you?" My mother was not finished. "Just remember, you're young. You get married, you stay married. You make your bed, you lie in it. You can't come home if things don't work out. You'll be on your own. Do you understand?" Her warning was sobering and designed to paint the stars in my eyes with the brush of life's reality. But neither of my parents realized just how much we were in love.

Later, my mother spoke to my father and gave her

advice. "Look, Joe, they want to get married. Let them get married before they 'have to' get married." There was a history of this in my mother's family, and she was afraid of a continuation of it in her daughters' lives.

Today I can understand their concern and their caution. We were teenagers. It seemed that no one could fathom young people our age having the depth of commitment to each other that we had. No one thought our marriage would last, but they were wrong. We were married for seventy years before Tommy passed away. Ultimately, Tommy spoke to my dad again and asked his permission for us to become formally engaged.

On September 17, 1950, Tommy gave me a diamond and we were officially betrothed.

SIXTEEN

Preparing to Be a Bride

Tommy resumed his tour of duty at Camp LeJeune, North Carolina. He was being retrained for a non-combat assignment possibly in Algeria or the South Pacific. It was also feasible that he might be assigned stateside, something I secretly hoped would occur.

Since Tommy was farther south once again, it extended his travel time for weekend visits. Rides were often difficult to acquire, and as the winter approached, inclement weather hindered travel. One weekend he could obtain a ride only as far as Ossining, New York. Having only enough money for the return trip on the train, he called his father to retrieve him.

Mr. Serino asked me if I wanted to go with him to Ossining, which I did, but when he stopped at the house for me, my parents forbid me to go. They didn't know Mr. Serino and weren't going to allow their naïve young daughter to get in the car with someone they had met only one time. I was disappointed, but Mr. Serino assured us that he understood and said he would bring Tommy right to our house.

Each weekend Tommy came home, we would spend time with each other's family. It was at this point that we began to refer to each other's parents as Mom and Dad, or a variation of that. I called Tommy's dad Pop, as Tommy did, and his mother Mom. Tommy called my father Dad, but for my mother he had a special name. He called her "Babe," saying she was his baby doll. Surprisingly, my conservative mother liked the nickname and so for the rest of her life she was Tommy's "Babe."

We spent many Saturday afternoons with Dolores and Johnny, whose company I truly enjoyed. Tommy was constantly teasing Johnny, who was such a good sport, and he was merciless to his sister, who was easily provoked, which resulted in a flood of cuss words (some I had never heard before, even from Aunt Eleanor) and curses upon all of Tommy's future generations. This was followed by uproarious laughter from Tommy, who loved to see his sister raging. The conclusion was always hugs and kisses and some final profanity directed at Tommy, followed by words of sympathy for me and my future with her brother.

It was great fun to pass the day with them. Dolores now was a new mother, as her first daughter was born in August, and seeing that beautiful little girl and the joy she brought to her parents was enriching. I wondered what it would be like to be a mother and see the serenity on Johnny's face reflected in Tommy's countenance.

Tommy's brother Jerry was also married, and his wife had a daughter in September of the same year, merely two weeks after Dolores. This prompted Tommy's father to predict that "Doris will have the first boy in the family." He then offered a fifty-dollar bond to the first daughter or daughter-in-law to have a boy.

Jerry's wife insisted on becoming pregnant again immediately to claim the honor of having the first boy. She was insanely jealous of me and once made the statement, "Mom loves Johnny, and Pop loves Doris, but no one loves me." She was a self-centered woman who proved to be an unfaithful companion to my poor brother-in-law. She succeeded in having the first boy, but before he was two years old, she left her husband and children for another man. No one ever heard from her again.

After the Christmas and New Year's holidays, it was time to begin planning for our wedding in earnest. We had chosen the date of July first for our wedding day. The Pirate Canoe Club was available for our reception, and Nativity Church was available for the ceremony, but most importantly, it was the first Saturday after my eighteenth birthday.

This was significant to me as a declaration to the world that I was no longer a starry-eyed teenager, but a woman mature enough to become a bride. To my parents it was essential, for although they saw me as a little girl—their little girl—the law recognized my right as an adult to make this decision for myself. It provided them both a hope that things would work out well for my marriage and a vindication of them if it did not. Their concerns over our youth remained, but we were prepared to begin wedding planning for the subsequent six months.

The first step was choosing my bridesmaids. Kay, as my only sister, would be my maid of honor, and Dolores would naturally be one of my bridesmaids. The other girls were a bit of a mystery. I didn't have that many friends, having been a shy girl and walking in the shadow of my sister for much of my brief high school experience.

I thought of Margaret Waligora. Although she was Kay's age, I knew her well as a member of the gang. She had always been kind to me and a good companion when I felt alone. I needed one more girl, but I didn't feel close enough to anyone to choose as a bridesmaid. Then I remembered Ida Cosa. She was perfect since I had been visiting Ida when I first saw Tommy. Even though I hadn't had a great deal of interaction with Ida over the last few years, she was more than honored to stand up for me as a bridesmaid.

So, one Saturday in early spring, the bride, bridesmaids, and the two mothers made an excursion to Newburgh in several cars and met at Scott's Dress Shop on Water Street. There I picked out my wedding gown and my bridesmaids chose their dresses. My mother and I had taken the bus down earlier so I could pick my wedding dress and decide on several styles of bridesmaids' gowns from which to choose. The bridesmaids picked the style while I chose the colors, then each girl decided which color they would wear.

I was having a rainbow wedding, so each attendant would wear a certain color dress and the groomsman with whom she walked would have a white coat, a white shirt, and a black bowtie. It was a joyous occasion, and everyone was enjoying themselves, except one. Tommy's mother was in one of her "moods" and was being as difficult as she could possibly be. She was uncooperative with everything, and nothing seemed to satisfy her. One dress was too tight on her, the next one too loose. The collar on this one was scratchy, while the hem line on the other one was too short. She didn't like blue or green or yellow or cerulean.

She finally decided on a short sleeved, square-necked, knee-length taupe dress that much resembled a burlap sack. We tried to convince her to choose something more flattering, but she stubbornly refused to change her mind. Dolores, much like Tommy, was brusque and direct in her approach. She said, "Ma, you look like an old lady in that dress. For goodness' sake, pick something else."

Unfortunately, the more opposition she received, the more unyielding she became. Dolores looked at me and shook her head. I responded with a "what can you do" look, and it was done.

The other girls each picked beautiful pastel colors. As the maid of honor, Kay's gown was slightly different from the bridesmaids'. She chose a strapless gown of blue frosted organdy with a matching shawl and a picture hat. Dolores, Margaret, and Ida selected yellow, orchid, and Nile green respectively, each with matching jackets and picture hats. The hats had a thin wire in the brim, and we molded them so the hats were heart shaped.

The flower girl was a cousin's child on the Serino side, Maria Potenza. She was to wear a pink frock with a bonnet. My mother chose an orchid dress with white accessories, and with her fair skin and red hair, she nearly outshined the bride.

I chose the most beautiful wedding gown I had ever seen. It was pure white and made of slipper satin, with an off-the-shoulder neckline trimmed with seed pearls and rhinestones, a fitted bodice, and a full skirt with a train. My fingertip veil was caught to a satin cap trimmed with seed pearls. The moment I stepped in front of the mirror, I knew I'd found the gown in which I would become Mrs. Thomas Serino. I felt like a princess.

As the day drew closer, two things remained: ordering the food for the reception and completing and mailing the invitations. We mailed over two hundred invitations, which was a monumental task requiring the efforts of various people over the course of several days. My mother, Kay, and I were the primary scribes, but Mom also enlisted the assistance of several friends, including Hattie and Mrs. McCoy.

We were able to host this many guests because weddings then didn't feature full dinners. We offered pizza, finger sandwiches, wine, and beer. Afterward there was wedding cake and a *guantiera* of Italian wedding cookies, complete with bags provided for guests to bring the matrimonial confections home to enjoy the next day while thinking of the newlywed couple.

My mother went to Café Aurora in Mount Carmel Square to order the sandwiches. This was a trip she despised. Mount Carmel Square was Poughkeepsie's "Little Italy," and there was a time when no one crossed the bridge on Mill Street to enter Mount Carmel Square unless you were Italian. Many people in this neighborhood knew my family because we'd lived in the square briefly in 1945. Some looked down on my parents as having a mixed marriage. Others who didn't know my family would see a random "Medigan" woman walking in the square and utter curses, hurl insults, or simply stare with antipathy. My mother generally avoided this area.

Ordinarily, she would have ordered the sandwiches from Filoia's in Union Square or Deneco's across the street. But the owners of Café Aurora were friends of Pop Serino, so he wanted the business to go to them. Consequently, my mother ordered several hundred sandwiches made on soft rolls with all the Italian delicacies. The purveyors of the café were good to her, providing a fair price, and because they were friends of the Serinos and would be attending the wedding, they provided not one but two *guantiera*—ninety pounds—of cookies as a wedding present.

June arrived. Replies to our invitations were pouring in with few negative responses. Final wedding arrangements—food, band, church, venue, honeymoon arrangements, and transportation—were complete. Everything seemed primed and ready for the big day. Tommy was able to obtain two weeks' leave, encompassing the week before the wedding and the week following.

My eighteenth birthday fell on a Tuesday, and to celebrate the day, Tommy and I went to city hall to purchase our marriage license. Tommy was not yet twenty-one, and men under the age of twenty-one couldn't obtain a marriage license without parental permission, so his father had to sign the papers giving him permission to marry. At eighteen a woman wasn't required parental permission, so I didn't need my father's signature. Tommy paid the two-dollar fee, and we were ready. Once the priest signed the license, we would be officially married in the eyes of the State of New York.

Thursday evening, we had our wedding rehearsal at the church. Afterward, my mother hosted a beautiful buffet at our apartment for the wedding party and assorted relatives. She also had a cake for me and made the night a celebration of my eighteenth birthday. My considerate mother had never missed a birthday party for Kay and me, and this year, despite the wedding responsibilities, was no exception.

My father wasn't feeling very well. He'd had surgery on his shoulder the week before and signed himself out of the hospital on Saturday. The doctor wouldn't discharge him, but he said, "My daughter is getting married this week, and I'm going home no matter what you say." So on Saturday night a taxicab pulled up in front of our house and Daddy got out. At the rehearsal that evening, the priest congratulated my father by slapping him on the back, unknowingly releasing waves of sharp pain from his shoulder that didn't subside until the next day.

I sat next to Tommy on the couch and my eyes scanned the room. My bridesmaids were all present, as were the guys who would stand up for Tommy, Hattie and Albert, Mr. and Mrs. McCoy, Aunt Betty, and my loving parents and sister, all in attendance at my eighteenth birthday celebration. In just three more days they would gather again to witness Tommy's and my union as husband and wife. It was a wonderful evening foreshadowing the glorious weekend just ahead. I had two more days to be Miss Messina, and Tommy was here to enjoy it with me.

SEVENTEEN
The Wedding

I was awakened by the sound of hard, driving rain against the roof and outer walls of our apartment. The torrential downpour was such that the street was barely visible from my bedroom window. My heart sank as I viewed the deluge with despair, the rainstorm washing my hopes of a sun-kissed matrimonial ceremony down the street into the gutter. I was wrapped in a melancholy robe of disappointment when a sudden resounding thunderclap shocked me into reality.

This was my wedding day, and I had no time to waste despairing the weather. I wrapped myself in my housecoat and went to the kitchen where my mother was making breakfast and my father was finishing his morning coffee. "Good morning, Doris," Mom said, unusually chipper that morning.

"Morning," came my gloomy response. Before taking my seat, I kissed my father on the forehead. "Morning, Daddy."

"Good morning, sweetie," was his simple reply.

"You'd better hurry, Doris, if you're going to make it to the eight o'clock mass," my mother warned.

She was right, of course. I couldn't attend a later mass and expect to have enough time to prepare for the wedding, and every bride was required to receive communion before her wedding. Moreover, Tommy was attending the later mass and I couldn't go with him. It was tradition. The groom couldn't see the bride before the wedding.

I quickly dressed and, because of the driving rain, decided not to comb out my hair for church. If I did, the rain would destroy all my efforts from the previous evening. So I covered my head with a kerchief tied tightly to keep the pin curls in place and positioned a hat over the kerchief so I wouldn't resemble an old washwoman at mass. Kay and I walked up the street, each carrying an umbrella angled against the tempest. Despite our best efforts, we were soaked when we arrived at Nativity Church, especially our feet, which had seemingly found every puddle along the way.

It was still raining hard, even harder than earlier, when mass ended. My heart sunk again as I realized there wasn't much hope for a not-sodden wedding day. We entered the house, and as we left our wet umbrellas in the stand near the door, my mother called, "I made you some breakfast, Doris!"

"Now, you have to eat a good breakfast today," she went on when I joined her in the kitchen. "You have a lot to do in the next few hours, and before you know it you'll be in the church with nothing in your stomach. I'll not have you fainting from hunger before you say, 'I do.'"

I was in no mood to resist, so I responded with a grunt as I sipped the coffee she had placed before me.

My parents seemed quite calm in view of the colossal

event taking place in less than five hours. My mother had good reason for tranquility. She'd planned everything to the smallest detail and set events in motion to be executed at precisely the proper time: dresses were laid out, having been cleaned and pressed before being retrieved. The flowers had been delivered to the church yesterday and placed in position at the altar, while the remaining flowers, bridal bouquets, corsages, and boutonnieres would be delivered today to our house by noontime.

Mom and Kay would leave for church before Daddy and me, and they would carry the flowers for each attendant. Each bridesmaid and groomsman would be dressing at their own house, and we would meet them in the narthex of the church by two o'clock to allocate the flowers and ascertain any modifications to ensure perfection on each member of the bridal party. Food would be delivered to the Pirate Canoe Club by three o'clock, and the staff would organize the means and timing of allocation to our guests. The band would arrive by four and be anticipating our entrance by five. My parents had prepared for everything—except the rain. I was despondent.

"What's the matter, sweetie?" my mother asked, startling me from my pensive state.

It didn't take great insight or existential knowledge to discern my disheartenment. I looked up at her and began to cry. "It's raining," was all I could say before the torrent of sobs overtook my voice.

My mother smiled. She smiled! My heart was breaking, my wedding day happiness was in jeopardy, and she was smiling! She put her arm around me and said, "It'll be fine, Doris, just you wait and see. You have five hours before the wedding, and it's raining so hard that it can't last all day."

"Besides," she continued, "it's good luck when it rains on a bride."

"Good luck? I'll be lucky if I don't drown in this downpour," I wept, giving full vent to my emotions.

My mother was unusually encouraging in this crisis, something I desperately needed. "Don't worry. We have cars to take everyone to church. Everything will be perfect. Just you wait and see. Now, eat something. It's normal to have such mixed-up emotions on your wedding day. Do you love Tommy?"

"Yes," I said, feeling the shroud of misery lifting from around my shoulders.

"Then just think about that and let everyone else worry about the rest, okay?"

"Okay, Ma," I whimpered, feeling like a kindergartner on the first day of school. I sipped my coffee but couldn't bring myself to eat anything. There was little space in my stomach for food with the kaleidoscope of butterflies I was housing.

Kay entered the kitchen as I was finishing and announced, "Did you guys see how hard it's raining outside? What are you going to do, Doris?"

I ran from the room in tears.

Mom looked incredulously at Kay and shook her head. "You know, sometimes it's just better not to talk."

"What?" Kay responded defensively. "What did I say wrong?"

Relatives began to arrive, and soon our little apartment was as busy as Grand Central Station. Many of our family came in from out of town and arrived early to aid the process in whatever manner necessary. My mother had set up a buffet, and guests were enjoying the antenuptial feast.

Aunt Betty had set up an ironing board in the parlor

and was ironing the train of my gown. It had arrived in plastic and the train was gathered at the bottom, collecting wrinkles. "You can't get married in a wrinkled gown," she announced and took it upon herself to remedy the situation.

I retired to the bathroom and enjoyed the solace of the bath, allowing the hot water to wash away my anxiety.

After my bath, Kay took the pin curls from my hair, which I had set the night before. If done correctly, we would merely need to comb it out and, once I put on my gown, coif my hair to the desired style. Then we would spray my hair into submission, not permitting one strand to shift from its position. Aunt Betty brought the gown to my room and assisted Kay and me with each stage of accoutre.

When I put on my wedding gown, I was spellbound by the image reflected in the mirror. Was it really me? The reflection in the mirror looked so angelic, so divinely wonderful—how could this be me? Could the mirror somehow take the inner joy I was experiencing and manifest it on the outside? I was radiant. Kay saw it too. She approached me slowly from behind, gently stroked my satin-appareled right arm, and said almost reverently, "You look beautiful, sis."

With hair, makeup, and gown all in proper order, Kay and I went to the parlor where the photographer was waiting. He began his work, carefully avoiding the multitude of relatives gathered. He snapped pictures of me standing in the parlor, looking in the mirror, and holding my bouquet. He seemed to have unlimited film. Then he took photos of me with all my family, in every possible combination and every possible situation. I was exhausted after the photoshoot but still had an entire wedding to accomplish.

My favorite pictures were of me pinning the corsage on

my mother. Her smile was magnificent, and the beautiful white roses complimented her orchid-colored gown perfectly. Then the photo of my father walking me out of the apartment. He was stoic as he took my arm for the last time as the only man in my life. I looked into his eyes and wondered about his thoughts. He didn't appear to be sad, but pensive. Was he wondering if he had done enough to prepare me for this moment?

"What are you thinking, Daddy?" I asked as we walked out the front door onto the porch.

"I was thinking how fortunate you are that the rain stopped an hour ago, and that we have this beautiful car to take you to the church so you don't wet your dress in any residual puddles," he said without a trace of emotion.

"I'm fortunate to have a mother and father like you," I said, my heart full of love for both.

"Let's get you to the car," Daddy replied, avoiding the sentimental conversation. Then he looked around. "Where's Merte?"

Ted Merte was a friend of my father. They played cards together, and he lived around the corner. He would be driving the car that would take my father and me to the church.

Ted, who'd been snatching some salami from the buffet table, came rushing outside. "I'm right here, Joe. I have the car windows down because it's so hot. I'll drive slowly so we don't mess up your hair, Doris."

Ted wasn't underestimating the temperature. When the rain stopped, the heat and humidity swept over the city like a blanket, making the air thick and causing heavy satin gowns to become uncomfortable. Nevertheless, I was thankful for the sunshine despite the heat that accompanied it.

We drove around the block and up Union Street to Nativity Church, passing the candy store where I first met Tommy. When Ted parked in front of the church, only a few people stood on the sidewalk. Most of the guests had already been seated in the church. All of my bridesmaids and groomsmen had arrived and were waiting in the vestibule. My father got out of the car and came around to open my door.

As I emerged, the people standing around applauded. I blushed and gathered my long train so Daddy could close the car door. "Are you ready to go into the church?" he asked.

"Yes, Daddy," I replied.

"Then let's go into the narthex." He seemed to understand the significance of this last ride we had just taken together.

As I ascended the steps on my father's arm, I realized how full the church was. Guests were seated from the front row to the back row, with dozens of people standing in the back. The bridesmaids had all received their cascade bouquets of gladiolas, and the groomsmen were all present with the exception of Jerry, who, as the best man, was with Tommy at the front of the church waiting in the sacristy with the priest.

The vocalist, Louise Armstrong, had just finished her rendition of "Ave Maria," and the church organist, Laurena Light began playing the "Wedding March." This was our cue to line up for the procession. As the song began, first to walk in was George Williams accompanying Margaret Waligora, followed by Don Lee escorting Ida Cosa. Next were my new brother- and sister-in-law, Johnny and Dolores Gallo. Finally, Kay, as my maid of honor, made the solo journey down the aisle. Immediately behind her were Joey

Cervone and Maria Potenza, the ring bearer and the flower girl.

Then, as my father and I appeared at the entrance to the sanctuary, the organist increased the volume on the "Wedding March," inspiring all the guests to stand.

"Are you ready, honey?" my father asked me.

"Yes, Daddy. You know that I am," I answered.

We walked slowly down the aisle to the approving looks of all in attendance. Then I saw him. Standing at the altar to the left of the priest was Tommy in a white tuxedo jacket, black pants, a white shirt, and a black bow tie. On his left collar he wore a small white rose as a boutonniere.

When our eyes met, Tommy smiled and I blushed. Daddy and I reached the front of the church, and I stood to the right of the priest while my father stood in the middle and Tommy to the left. The organist finished the song, and the priest began the mass.

"In nomine patris, filii, et spiritus sanctus."

The congregation responded, "Amen."

"Dominis vobiscum," recited the priest, followed by the congregations' response, *"Et cum spiritu tuo."* The wedding mass was brief, lasting about thirty minutes, and before I realized it was over, the priest said in English, "I now pronounce you man and wife. You may kiss your bride."

At this declaration, Tommy swept me into his arms and kissed me.

The organ burst into the wedding recessional song, and we turned to walk slowly down the aisle, followed immediately by the ring bearer and flower girl, then the rest of the bridal party. As we reached the end of the aisle, Miss Tilly, the housekeeper at the rectory, stopped us and said to me, "Doris, this is the most beautiful wedding we've ever had at Nativity Church."

I thought so too. The photographer was waiting at the front door of the church and took our picture as we exited.

We descended the stairs, now husband and wife, and proceeded to the car awaiting us at the curb. Ted Merte had the back door open, prepared for our entrance. Four additional cars with drivers waited for their designated bridesmaids and groomsmen, with each couple having their own car and driver.

The cars had been decorated by the groomsmen when the rain ended and the cars dried, and now they were lined up so that the bridal party led the motorcade, with the car carrying the bride and groom last in the procession. Our car had streamers and cans attached, as well as a large sign in the back window announcing "Just Married" to the entire city.

As Tommy and I slid into the back of the car, Ted took his place in the driver's seat, then waited for the parade to begin. Tommy put his arm around me, and his arm caught the veil of my hat and tore it slightly from the cap.

"Dammit, Tommy! You tore my veil!" I chastised, upset since the veil was borrowed.

"I'm sorry, Doris. I didn't mean it. I was just trying to put my arm around you," he pleaded.

"Well, be more careful, will you?" I scolded.

Ted Merte laughed loudly. "Will you look at that. They're not even married five minutes and already they're fighting!" His laughter was so contagious that I couldn't continue my outrage. Tommy and I laughed, then Tommy kissed me gently.

The procession began as the car carrying George and Margaret pulled away from the curb, and the horns began blaring in a joyous chorus announcing to the world that Tommy and I were married. We drove down Union Street, over South Clover Street past my house, and on to Mill Street. From Mill Street we traveled to Bridge Street, which we followed to Main Street.

Along every street well-wishers waved and shouted congratulations and salutations. I felt like President Roosevelt when he would drive through Poughkeepsie on his way to his mansion in Hyde Park. It was exhilarating being applauded by strangers, people agreeing that what we had done was worthy of praise. We received their blessings for a successful marriage, and every greeting contained a hope for a happy life.

We were heading to the photo studio on Main Street, where the photographer would take a multitude of wedding pictures—photos taken of the wedding party, the Serino family, and the Messina family, with photos in black and white but several in color. Color film was extremely expensive at that time, but because of the rainbow theme in our wedding, the photographer insisted that several photos be taken in color to capture the beauty that would be lost in tones of gray.

Afterward, the cars took us to the Pirate Canoe Club for the reception, where our guests would be awaiting our arrival. Most guests had walked from the church to the reception since it was only a few blocks away. While the reception didn't formally begin until five, the invitees could pass the time at the bar or on the deck overlooking the Hudson River.

We first drove up Main Street before continuing down toward the river. I looked at Tommy's face and wondered if he was as excited as I was. "Did you like our wedding, Tommy?" I wanted to know what he was thinking, how he was feeling, but I didn't know how to ask.

"What? Well, sure I did," was his vague reply.

"What was your favorite part?" I prodded, trying to get more of an answer from him.

Tommy leaned back against the seat and turned to me. "My favorite part was seeing you appear at the door. I knew then that you really did love me and would never leave me," he said softly.

Surprised, I responded, "Tommy! You know that I love you and would never forsake you, never desert you." I still didn't understand how deeply the abandonment of his past had affected his psyche.

"I know. I know that now. You are my wife, forever. Nothing can change that."

I laid my head on Tommy's shoulder, enthralled by the magic of the moment. I was living a dream, sitting next to my knight in shining armor in our matrimonial chariot. We were on our way to begin our life together, a life and a love that would endure for seven decades.

EIGHTEEN

The Reception

The motorcade arrived at the Pirate Canoe Club, and when we exited the cars, the air felt much cooler. Although it was ninety degrees and there was still three hours until sundown, the breeze wafting from the river made the sultry evening bearable. The venue, which was shaded and positioned directly on the bank of the river, was two stories and offered a tavern complete with tables, chairs, a bar, and barstools on the first floor, while an enormous banquet hall filled the second floor. Each floor had a covered porch extending over the river providing an escape from the conviviality for patrons requiring a reprieve.

Our reception was being hosted on the second floor, and as the bridal party ascended the creaky, wooden staircase, the din of numerous conversations and the clamor of servers shuffling trays of food and the band beginning their warm-up all contributed to the anticipation of the celebration.

We entered the ballroom, and I surveyed the accommodations and observed a long table with a banner posted directly behind that bore our names: "Tom and Doris." This table would be our seats of honor for the evening. On either side of the table was two large *guantiera* of cookies, weighing forty-five pounds each. They were filled to overflowing with every Italian wedding confection imaginable, all wrapped in cellophane and fastened with a pink ribbon. Centered on the table but slightly adjacent to our seats was an ornate, four-tiered wedding cake that was listing slightly from the heat. A white cake with butter cream frosting, it too was wrapped in clear cellophane to protect it from the onslaught of flying insects.

Along the adjoining wall to our right were the tables reserved for food. A keg of beer sat at either end, already tapped and ready. Servers were carrying in platters of finger sandwiches—small, soft rolls filled to the bursting point with salumi and Italian cheeses. This was followed by tray after tray of hot pizza. Tables and folding chairs were scattered throughout the hall, and each table held a bottle of wine as a welcome gift to our guests. Not one of our four hundred attendees would leave hungry.

In the far corner, opposite the head table where Tommy and I sat, was the three-piece band conducted by Pete Leone. Pete was a coworker of my father, and his band was rumored to be proficient at contemporary dance music as well as traditional Italian favorites. As the music began, guests poured in from the tavern below and found their places at the tables. Some of them approached the head table to greet Tommy and I and offer their congratulations and "envelopes."

We had no table for gifts because all wedding gifts were cash. No one would ever bring a toaster or an arrangement of flatware to an Italian wedding. It was unheard of. I carried a satin purse with me, and every envelope was deposited into it.

This was the reason Pop Serino insisted that Tommy and I sit at the table, to ensure that each guest had access to us to offer their best wishes and cash gifts. It became a bone of contention as the reception progressed, though. Each time Tommy and I left the table to dance or get some food or a drink, Pop Serino would hurry over and say, "No, no. You gotta sit at the table. People wanna see you."

Finally, I went to the band to make a request. I wanted them to play "It's Too Soon to Know," the song that had become so special to Tommy and me. When they began to play, Tommy was en route to join me for the dance, but Pop Serino intercepted him.

"Where you go?" he asked. "You gotta sit at the table. People wanna see you."

"Dammit, Pop," Tommy said. "I intend to enjoy my wedding today, okay?" He then took me in his arms and we danced the next few songs together.

After the third song, I said to Tommy, "We'd better go back to the table."

He scowled. "No, Doris. I'm getting a little tired of his nonsense. We're not running away, we're just dancing."

"He means well," I said quietly. "He just wants to make sure that all the guests feel appreciated. We are the most important couple here today, remember? We're the reason everyone came today, and it's important that we greet everyone and make time for each person to wish us well."

As Tommy looked at me, the anger melted from his face. He smiled and said, "That's why you are his favorite," and then spun me around.

As we were heading back to the table, my father

stopped us. "I want to take my little girl for a spin around the dance floor. Do you mind, Tommy?"

"Not at all, Dad," Tommy replied.

Daddy whisked me onto the dance floor, and we danced a waltz around the hall. He kept me through the next dance, and finally looked at me and asked, "Are you happy?"

It seemed like a curious question to me. "Yes, Daddy. I'm very happy."

He nodded. "Remember this. You have a husband now. He comes first. I come second."

At hearing this, I understood what my father had been thinking throughout the day. Each time I'd seen him, he'd seemed lost in thought, pensive and struggling to grasp a principle that was both uncomfortable and necessary. By declaring to the priest that he was the one giving me to be married to Tommy, my father was relinquishing his position as primary authority, covering, and custodian in my life. He was no longer my protector, my guardian. That place had been taken by someone else, and he wanted me to know that he accepted this new status and that I must also.

"I understand, Daddy," I responded. "But you'll always be my first love. You know that."

Daddy smiled, swung me around, and said, "Let's get you back to the table before your father-in-law has a conniption."

I laughed and held his arm as we returned to the head table.

Several people were waiting there to greet us. There were so many hugs and kisses for me and handshakes and winks for Tommy. Men told Tommy what a lucky guy he was, and women told me how beautiful I looked and how moving the ceremony had been. We greeted every person

THROUGH MY MOTHER'S EYES

with love and respect, and collected a bounty of well wishes.

Then I happened to glance up and a couple was approaching the table—Eleanor DiPilco and her date. I should have known that she would be invited because her mother and Mom Serino were good friends. I just didn't think that she would attend. While I didn't know the fellow escorting her, I knew Eleanor well enough to be on guard.

She approached us. "Oh, Tommy, my Tommy. I wish you all the luck in the world. It was so nice to see you again," she said and offered her cheek for Tommy to kiss.

He placed a respectful peck on her cheek as I extended my hand to Eleanor. She glanced at my hand and turned, then took her date by the arm and walked away without saying a word to me.

My face flushed with anger. That little vixen. I wanted to scratch her eyes out. When I looked at Tommy, he laughed, and I was rendered speechless. He took me in his arms and comforted me, quietly cautioning me, "Careful, Doris. Murder still carries the death penalty in New York." Then he kissed me on the cheek. "Come on. Let's dance."

The evening passed quickly, and with the setting sun came evening breezes from the river and a chorus of bull-frogs, cicadas, and crickets that could be heard from the porch overlooking the water. Inside the great hall, the sounds of celebration continued into the night, and soon it was time for the "Grand March" and the farewell send-off of the newlyweds. This was a huge event performed at every wedding, and it required full audience participation.

The one appointed "Grand Marshall"—someone with skill and expertise to coordinate the movements of the crowd—would signal the band to begin the accompanying music. Our Grand Marshall was Joe Filoia—redheaded Joe

Filoia, known as "Red," since there were several Joe Filoias around town. He owned a barber shop in Union Square and was well known for his skill as a marshal of the "Grand March."

Red took his place near the band and shouted over the microphone, announcing the beginning of the Grand March. "Where are the bride and groom?" he bellowed, his voice echoing through the room.

Tommy and I waved at him, and I quickly took the orchid out of my bouquet. I would be wearing the orchid as a corsage on my honeymoon, but the bouquet would be launched into the crowd at the end of the Grand March, to be kept by the lucky girl who captured it. We hurried over to Red and stood on his right side.

He pointed at people as they approached him and commanded them to move in the direction he pointed. "Two this way, two that way. Now three this way, three that way. Two more to the right, and two more to the left. Let's do four this way and four more the other way." Red was shouting orders in tune with the music like a performer singing his lines in a Broadway musical. The people were laughing and lining up, some becoming humorously confused and redirected by helping hands, until everyone in the hall was lined up along the wall. Red then called out, "Hands together! Form an arch!"

Each guest standing face-to-face with another would join both hands and raise them up over their heads. This formed a giant archway surrounding the entire banquet hall and ending at the front entrance. Tommy and I then joined hands and entered the human pergola. Side by side we traversed the unbroken funnel of arms until we reached the doorway.

As we passed by, each couple unlocked hands and gathered toward the front of the hall in hopes of catching the coveted bouquet. At the door we stopped, and to the thunderous applause of four hundred wedding guests I catapulted my flowers in the direction of the single ladies crowded together on the left. We descended the stairs, and I heard cheers and merriment, so the flowers had landed safely. Later I would learn that the wedding reception continued even after Tommy and I left. Everyone was enjoying themselves so much that my mother hired the hall and the band for another hour!

My father was waiting for us in the parking lot. "We have to hurry," he said. "It's five minutes to ten, and the train leaves for New York at ten twenty."

So Tommy and I piled into the backseat of Daddy's Kaiser and he rushed us to my house a few blocks away. We had just enough time to throw off our wedding clothes and redress in travel clothes, pick up our suitcases we had prepacked for the trip, and get back in the car for the ride to the train station. While we were doing this, Daddy was counting out money from my satin bag while recording the name and the amount of each gift in a book.

Tommy was waiting for me when I came out of the bedroom.

Daddy handed him a roll of cash and said, "We'll take care of the rest of the gifts later, but take this with you to enjoy. After all, you only get one honeymoon."

"Thanks, Daddy," I said and kissed his cheek.

"Okay, kids, let's get going. You don't want to miss your train. It's a long walk to the city!"

We hurried to the car and arrived at the train station just as the conductor was calling out, "All aboard!"

I turned to my father and threw my arms around him. "Goodbye, Daddy. Thank you for everything."

"Okay, sweetie." Then with misty eyes, he said, "Have fun and come back safe."

"We will, Daddy." Emotion welled up in me, and Tommy's voice brought me back to reality.

"Come, Doris, or we're going to miss the train."

We ran to the train, carrying our baggage, and boarded just as the train began to pull away from the platform. The train began moving down the track and picked up speed, making it difficult to walk the aisle to our seats. When we finally sat down, I breathed a sigh of relief. We had made it. We were on our way. I settled back into my seat and glanced around the car only to realize it was full of service men.

Upon closer examination, I realized I was the only woman on board!

NINETEEN
The Honeymoon

The train ride to New York City was terribly awkward. I never dreamed I'd be the only woman on a train car full of service men. I felt so out of place. One of Tommy's friends from Camp LeJeune who had been a guest at our wedding was also on the train. When he saw Tommy and me, he greeted us with loud congratulations, informing everyone on the train that we were just married. All the guys were talking among themselves and joking. Amid their side glances and snickers and occasional bursts of laughter, I knew what they were talking about. Tommy thought it outrageously funny, but I was embarrassed. It was the longest trip to the city I had ever taken.

Finally, we arrived at Grand Central Station. After leaving the terminal, we walked the short distance to the Biltmore Hotel. It was a magnificent structure, built in the Italian Renaissance Revival style, on Madison Avenue in Midtown Manhattan. We walked under the street, along the tiled walkway, to the reception area in the basement of the hotel, then ascended the spacious staircase to the ground floor, where we saw the main dining area and the elegant Palm Court. The sight of Palm Court took my breath away. I had never seen anything so magnificent.

When Tommy and I approached the desk to sign in for our room, I was attempting to take in all the opulence around us so I could cherish it forever in my memory.

A bellhop approached Tommy. "I'll take your suitcase, son. Anything for newlyweds," he said.

Tommy stared at him. "How did you know that we were newlyweds?"

The man grinned. "Son, you got the guilty look all over your face." When Tommy reddened, the bellhop laughed. "Right this way, sir."

We took the elevator to the sixteenth floor of the twenty-three-story building. When we entered our room, I was again overwhelmed with the grandeur of this majestic structure. Our suite was spacious yet warm and comforting. Large windows were situated on two walls, and the window facing Madison Avenue had a luxurious window seat with plush cushions in deep burgundy to contrast the pearl-white draperies. The soft lighting, thick carpets, and private bath contributed to the sense of royalty I was feeling. I was truly a princess in the palace of my dreams with my prince by my side—living a fairy tale I never wanted to end.

Tommy tipped the bellhop, closed the door, and approached me. He took me in his arms, kissed me, and said softly, "I'll bathe first, then I'll wait for you here. Take your time."

As he entered the bathroom and closed the door, I suddenly realized that this was my wedding night. A panic came over me. I had very little idea of what was going to happen or how. Parents at that time were extremely hesitant to speak with their children about sex. I had heard things from Kay and my friends, but I didn't really know anything.

My anxiety soared when Tommy opened the bathroom door. I was so startled that my feet nearly jumped off the floor. Tommy was in his robe, his hair combed and freshly shaven.

"I cleaned the tub and drew a warm bath for you, Doris," he said tenderly. "Take your time. We have all night."

Petrified, I could only squeak out, "Okay."

I entered the bathroom and took the longest bath in the history of bathing. Then I dried myself, brushed my teeth, and fixed my hair. With nothing more to do, I looked at the teddy l had chosen for tonight lying across the chair and wished I had my flannel pajamas instead.

When I left the bathroom, Tommy was sitting up in the bed with the covers over his lap. The room was dimly lit, as he had extinguished all the lights but one. I headed for the window seat.

"Where are you going?" he asked.

"I just wanted to take a look at the view from the window." I sat on the soft cushion of the window seat and peeked outside. "Oh, Tommy, the view of Madison Avenue is incredible." Truly it was a spectacular view, and I was glad there was so much to observe. I sat watching drunken sailors, taxi cabs discharging fares, and the general traffic in and out of Grand Central Station.

Several times Tommy said gently, "Come to bed, honey,"

"Okay," I responded, but I remained seated at the window.

Thankfully, Tommy was patient with me. He had received good advice from a counselor at Camp LeJeune.

When Tommy had gone to him to ask permission to leave the base, the counselor asked, "Why do you want to leave?"

"Because I'm going to get married," Tommy replied.

"Why do you want to get married?" the counselor asked. "Why buy the cow when you can get the milk for free?"

"And what happens when you can't get the milk for free?" Tommy asked him.

"I guess you get married," chuckled the counselor, who then approved his two weeks leave. He then advised Tommy concerning the wedding night, "When you get married, don't rush your wife. Too many men make that mistake. Let it be on her time. She'll let you know when she's ready. Don't rush her, because then it doesn't go well, especially with someone who isn't experienced."

So Tommy didn't rush me at all. But he was ready.

I sat on the window seat for the next hour and a half, watching the silent traffic pass. When I glanced over at Tommy, who was silent, he was sound asleep. I tiptoed over to the bed and carefully lifted the covers, then crawled into bed. I slept peacefully the entire night, and we didn't get together until the next morning.

The next day, we took the bus to Atlantic City directly from the Biltmore Hotel. We exited the building from the main entrance on 43rd Street, where the bus from Port Authority received passengers. This gave us the opportunity to see the hotel from the outside. Its façade was limestone, brick, granite, and terracotta, and above the fourth floor, the building was U-shaped with inward rooms facing a light court on the north, south, and east sides. The splendor of the building has stayed with me, and I felt so sad when it was closed for demolition in 1981.

The bus ride to our Atlantic City hotel was quick, and

we arrived by midmorning. Tommy had only a few days left of his leave, so we needed to make the best use of our time together. There were no casinos in Atlantic City at that time. It was like a playland—a festival atmosphere complete with a boardwalk, arcades, stores open all night long, and carnival rides near the beach. We went out at all hours of the night and enjoyed everything available to us.

Since it was Independence Week—the Fourth of July holiday was on Wednesday—this was the busiest time of the year for the resort area. I had made reservations months beforehand, so I was confident our room would be waiting for us. But when we arrived at the hotel desk and I presented my reservation confirmation, the clerk informed us that no deposit had been included in the request, so no room had been retained for us. I began to panic, and tears flooded my eyes at the possibility of my honeymoon ending before it started.

Taking a deep breath, I held out the confirmation I had received. "Well, what can be done about this?"

The clerk looked it over. "There was obviously some miscommunication on our part, Mrs. Serino. Let's see what we can do." He and another clerk poured over the registry and finally found us a tiny room on the second floor. We had our own bathroom, but it was connected to the hallway bathroom available to other hotel guests. Still, we had a room and the crisis was over. It was then I realized that this was the first time someone had called me "Mrs. Serino."

The porter approached us. "I'll take your bags. Anything for newlyweds. When did you folks get married?"

Tommy and I responded in unison, but with different answers. I said, "Yesterday," while he teased, "Last week."

The porter laughed. "This way, please."

After arriving at our room, we quickly unpacked and

went to the boardwalk. We hadn't eaten yet today and were famished.

"What do you want for breakfast?" Tommy asked.

"Pork chops," I answered.

"Pork chops? That's not breakfast."

I smiled. "Well, that's what I want."

Tommy never forgot that my first breakfast as his wife was pork chops.

We spent the rest of the day enjoying the boardwalk, shops, and arcades, and didn't return to our hotel until dark. Then we relaxed in our room with a small bottle of wine we had purchased, Tommy in his underwear and I in a beautiful new salmon-colored nightgown that was rather sheer.

With a grin, Tommy, knowing that I wasn't really a drinker, challenged me, "If you drink that whole bottle down, I'll run out and get you another bottle dressed like this."

I laughed. "Okay. Just like you are." After drinking the remaining half bottle of wine, I walked over to the door, opened it, and said, "There you go, Mr. Serino. On your way."

Tommy walked to the door, and before I knew what was happening, he grabbed me, pushed me into the hallway, and closed and locked the door.

Standing in the corridor in a sheer nightgown, I hammered on the door with my fist. "Tommy, open this door—now!"

Suddenly, I heard footsteps. I turned in horror to see the porter coming up the hallway. "Tommy, let me in!" I yelled. "The porter is coming!"

On the opposite side of the door, Tommy was laughing hard.

The porter passed me with a huge grin on his face. Keeping his eyes politely forward, he said, "Good evening, Mrs. Serino."

This was the second time someone referred to me as Mrs. Serino. I was so embarrassed. I wanted to crown my new husband. I should have known then what life would be like with him. It was never dull.

We stayed in Atlantic City until Wednesday, then returned to Poughkeepsie. We argued on the train on the way home and weren't speaking when we arrived. Tommy had to return to Camp LeJeune on Sunday, so we knew we couldn't stay angry very long. That was a tearful goodbye, because now I was sending my *husband* away.

Some things felt unchanged after the honeymoon. I was still living with my parents, and Tommy would come home each weekend. This continued through the month of July, and in August Tommy received his orders to go overseas. He would be stationed in Guam. I had never heard of Guam before, so Tommy explained that it was somewhere between Hawaii and China, which meant it was very far away from me. He assured me that he would be there only about a year and that he wouldn't be in harm's way.

Twenty days after being given his orders, Tommy boarded ship for the South Pacific on Labor Day weekend. I wouldn't see him again until November 1952.

After Tommy left for Guam, my life continued as if I was still single. I worked at the pocketbook factory, lived with my parents, and went to the movies on Friday nights with my sister. I received letters from Tommy frequently, but not daily as before. The overseas mail sometimes took a week or more to reach home.

One thing was different this time. Every Sunday morning while Tommy was away, Pop Serino came to visit me. He never had coffee and never stayed long, but he also never failed to visit and see how I was doing. He genuinely cared for me and my well-being.

In December 1951, I was admitted to Saint Francis Hospital with a hemorrhage. They were painting the second floor of the hospital at that time, where my room was located, so they moved all the patients on my floor to the first floor, leaving us in the drafty hallway for long periods of time. As a result, before the doctor could perform all the tests needed, I developed pneumonia. I was in the hospital for a month and was left with scars on my lungs, making me susceptible to pneumonia for the rest of my life.

During that hospital stay, Pop Serino visited me every night. He would come after work, just before visiting hours, and would charm the nurses to allow him to see me. He also sent a huge basket of flowers that stood almost three feet tall.

One nurse came to my room and commented, "Oh my. Somebody must really love you. Look at these flowers. I've never seen such a beautiful bouquet."

"They're from my father-in-law," I told her.

"Is that the man who comes to see you every night?"

"Yes."

She smiled. "Well, honey, that man truly loves you."

The time passed slowly, but eventually November 1952 came and Sergeant Tommy Serino returned home. He and I could now begin our lives together as husband and wife, even though we had already been married fifteen months.

TWENTY

After Guam

Tommy had taken very little leave time while in Guam, so he exercised his option to sell back the remaining days for cash. With this, plus his savings and discharge bonus, we had enough money to put toward an apartment. Unfortunately, apartments were nearly impossible to find in Poughkeepsie in 1952, and despite our best efforts, we were obliged to live with my parents. My family was very gracious about the situation and made room for us, but it was slightly crowded with five people in close quarters. We did this for eight months before an apartment became available.

Tommy began working with his father and apprenticed as a bricklayer. That required six months to become vested, then he was able to join Local #44 of the bricklayers, masons, and plasterers union in 1953. He worked as a union mason for forty-three years.

With Tommy's job locations being inside and outside the city, we had to purchase an automobile. At the time, Kay was dating Jimmy Sabia, who owned a used car lot.

He had told me, "Don't worry, Doris. When Tommy gets out of the service, I'll fix you up with a good car." He sold us a 1941 Plymouth for three hundred dollars.

It was a lemon. Each morning, I would go outside with Tommy to assist him in starting the car. I would get in the driver's seat while he pushed the car down the incline, and I would pop the clutch. Tommy would then trade places with me and drive to work. We didn't have that car long before we traded it in for a more reliable vehicle from O'Hara Motors. We kept this vehicle until we bought the only brand-new car we ever owned, a 1956 Oldsmobile.

Tommy was so proud of the Oldsmobile. Extremely cautious with it, he would park it away from the immediate construction area to prevent any potential damage. But then one day, a big shot from New York City came to inspect Tommy's job site and parked his car at the top of a small hill. He neglected to engage the parking brake, resulting in the car rolling backward and crashing into our car. Tommy saw it all happen from the scaffold where he was working. He watched in horror as our beautiful automobile was reduced to scrap metal. After this, Tommy said, "That's it. No more new cars." We purchased only used cars thereafter.

When Tommy came home from Guam and began working as a bricklayer, I had quit my job at the pocketbook factory and become a full-time homemaker. Tommy arrived home just one week before Thanksgiving, so we spent the holiday with my family since we were living with them. At Christmas we spent some of the day with my family and some of the day with the Serinos.

Tommy's family had begun to celebrate the holidays together. Mom and Pop Serino had a new apartment on Church Street, and Dolores and Jerry were both married with children, so they had new reasons to celebrate. Mom Serino always cooked, to everyone's satisfaction, but Tommy never wanted to stay long with his family. Even when we alternated the holidays, Thanksgiving with the Messinas and then Christmas with the Serinos, and the next year vice versa, Tommy still wanted to leave his parents' house early and we would go to my parents' apartment.

My mother loved the holidays, especially Christmas, and always had plenty of company. The first Christmas Tommy was home was no exception. Aunt Betty and Uncle Okey, and Uncle Santo and Aunt Marie were there. Many friends would stop by throughout the day. Ted Merte, Lena and Bill, and Hattie and Albert were among them. Tommy seemed calm—quite sedate, actually. He was no longer anxious around my family and the crowds of company. Rather the opposite, he seemed to enjoy the company and receive them as his own. It was as though Tommy had truly come home.

After the holidays, we fell into a blissful marital routine. I would wake early each morning with Tommy and fix his breakfast and pack his lunchbox, a routine I would follow for the next forty-three years. At night we would play cards or checkers or sometimes we'd simply watch TV—that is, if there wasn't too much interference. Tommy would go to bed by ten because he rose so early in the morning.

On Friday nights we usually went to the movies. Occasionally there was a dance at the Italian Center, and we'd all go together, Mom and Dad, Tommy and I, and Kay and her present boyfriend. On Saturday afternoons Tommy sometimes worked a side job for extra money. This was frowned upon by the union, but it was general knowledge that everyone did it. If Tommy wasn't working, Saturday afternoon was our time for visiting. We would visit Tommy's sister and her family, or Aunt Tessie and Uncle Mike, or we would take a large jar of coins to his mother's apartment and play cards with her and a few of her friends. She always had coffee and dessert and lots of laughs.

Sunday was church and dinner with my parents. When summertime came, there were the Sunday picnics at Lake Walton. Occasionally Mom Serino or Aunt Tessie and Uncle Mike would join us. It was wonderful to see my uncles and aunts and Tommy's uncles and aunts enjoying the time spent together. Our families had definitely grown into one large unit.

In June 1953, Pop Serino paid us a visit. He had good news for us. His cousin had an apartment available on Church Street that would be perfect for Tommy and me. It was a four-room apartment on the second floor, complete with a porch to sit outside on warm summer days.

We took the rental without question. Daddy went over and painted and wallpapered through the entire apartment, and I purchased all new furniture, bed linens, and draperies. The apartment looked beautiful, and we moved in the beginning of July.

But on our first night in the apartment, as we sat in the kitchen playing cards, we saw a cockroach. Then two, then ten, and soon the kitchen was alive with cockroaches. We hadn't noticed them before, but we'd only been there during the day while the sun was up. Now that it was evening, the cockroaches decided to lay their claim to the kitchen.

We didn't realize the extent of the infestation at first, but as the days passed, we learned that while we rented the apartment, the cockroaches owned it. Every time I took out a pot or pan to cook, I would have to chase a roach from it, then wash it before it could be used. Tommy and I would sit down to supper, and we'd see a roach or two walking up the wall. One day while my mother and I were sitting on the porch, I noticed through the window of the neighbor's apartment in her baby's bedroom there were cockroaches crawling in the baby's bed. I tried buying roach paste, but with serious infestation, the paste was useless.

I called the landlord and told him of the dilemma. "You've got to do something about this problem. We're walking away with cockroaches."

The landlord came over a short time later with a can of spray. I was incredulous. "What the hell are you going to do with that?" I would have moved immediately, but there were no apartments available in the city, and I had just purchased four rooms of new furniture, so I couldn't move back with my parents. We were stuck.

I complained to the landlord numerous times, but he did nothing. He merely grew angry with me, calling me ungrateful. I told him I would move the first opportunity that came along. "I have all new furniture," I said. "I'm afraid it'll become bug infested." The landlord was furious with us, and when we moved, he never spoke to us again.

The opportunity to move came in October 1953 when Tommy's brother Jerry's wife left him. They lived next to Dietrich and Martin's Meat Market on Union Street, and I immediately went and spoke to the landlord, requesting to rent the apartment. Having known me all my life, he was pleased to do that, and he said if we were willing to clean the apartment, we could move in immediately. Daddy again painted and wallpapered the apartment, and I gave it a thorough cleaning. Within the week, we moved from the "roach hotel" to our new apartment at 148 Union Street. We lived there until 1957.

TWENTY-ONE

First Child

On a cold, damp April evening in 1956, Tommy and I had finished dinner and he was on the couch in the parlor reading the evening paper while I finished cleaning the kitchen. We were both quite anxious, anticipating a phone call from Dr. Perino. Two days prior we had gone to his office and I had taken a blood test, the Friedman test to be precise, which took forty-eight hours before the results were available.

I was startled from my thoughts by the ringing phone, and I hurried to respond. "Hello?"

"Is this Mrs. Serino?" asked the voice on the phone.

"Yes, it is."

"This is Dr. Perino's office with the results of your blood test. The test came back positive. Congratulations, Mrs. Serino, you are having a baby."

A wave of emotion swept over me. After five years of trying to get pregnant, we finally had good news! "Thank you," I said, remembering the person on the phone. I hung up the receiver and hurried to the parlor.

Tommy was sitting at full attention. "Well, what is it?" was all he could say.

"It was a positive test. I'm going to have a baby."

Tommy leaped from the couch and shouted, "Yippee! I'm going to be a father!" He embraced me as tears of joy flowed freely from my eyes.

"Let's go tell my parents," I said.

Mom, Daddy, and Kay lived across the street, so I grabbed my coat and we hurried down the stairs. When we reached the first floor, Hattie, who lived in the apartment there, opened her door and said, "Congratulations, Doris. I heard the good news!" Then she looked at Tommy and chuckled.

"Maybe we don't have to cross the street to tell my parents," I teased him. "Maybe they heard you too."

Mom and Dad were thrilled that they would soon be grandparents. Kay was home too, and I asked her to be the baby's godmother. She hugged me tightly, full with emotion.

After that, we drove up to Church Street to tell Tommy's mother the good news. Pop Serino was there when we arrived. He was rarely home in the evenings, so this was a fortunate occurrence. When we told them we were expecting, both reacted favorably. Mom was excited, but Pop was brimming with happiness. "It's a gonna be a boy and you gonna calla him Jerry!" he declared.

"But, Pop, Jerry's son is already called Little Jerry," I protested. "We couldn't have another Jerry in the family."

"You gonna calla him Jerry," he repeated, undaunted. "Fursta boy always nameda after father's father."

There was no sense in trying to discuss it further, so I just hugged him and said, "I love you, Pop."

We were so excited that both Tommy and I had a difficult time getting to sleep that night. We were going to be parents. I couldn't have been happier.

A week passed before I went to see Dr. Perino. We went in the evening so that Tommy and I could go together. There were no appointments then. Patients simply entered the outer office and waited their turn. The doctor examined me and said that everything looked good, and I had reason to be optimistic. Nevertheless, he did caution me, "I'm not going to promise you that this pregnancy is going to work, because your uterus is tilted at an extreme angle. How the baby grows will determine if the pregnancy is successful. If you make it past the first three months, then you should have no problems."

We saw the doctor monthly for the remainder of the pregnancy, and the baby grew strong and healthy. The doctor's concerns were satisfied within the first month. He estimated that I was already past the first trimester by May and assigned a due date of the first week of October. The summer was long and hot, and I gained a tremendous amount of weight, too much for my small frame. This complicated even the simplest tasks. Washing dishes became a challenge, as my enlarged belly prevented me from reaching the hot- and cold-water controls without pressing against the sink. It strained my back, and the baby did not appreciate this and would kick back in protest. Tommy came to my rescue and would wash the dishes while I dried. Sleeping also became cumbersome, and I frequently moved to the couch during the night so I wouldn't disturb Tommy. Brief naps during the day became my salvation.

October came and went, and it was getting close to Thanksgiving. The doctor had miscalculated the baby's due date, but I could tell the time of parturition was approach-

THROUGH MY MOTHER'S EYES

ing. The baby, who had been very active, began to quiet, and I could feel him move into position for birth. The Monday of Thanksgiving week, the doctor said to me, "Well, Doris, it looks like you'll be eating your turkey in the hospital this year."

"Oh no I won't," I protested. "I've gone this far. I'm going to be home for Thanksgiving."

We spent the holiday with my parents, and I ate all day long. The next day my mother called to have us over for dinner again since there were leftovers, so Tommy and I went, and I again ate my fill. Then around three o'clock in the morning, I awoke with nausea, diarrhea, and vomiting. The labor pains began, and I started timing them. Tommy was scheduled to go hunting Saturday morning, so I didn't wake him.

When the contractions became more frequent, I called the doctor, who told me to meet him at the hospital. I attempted to rouse Tommy from sleep, but he awoke groggy and disoriented.

"Is it time to go hunting already?" he said.

"Nope, it's time to go to the hospital," I responded.

Instantly Tommy was fully awake. When we arrived at Saint Francis Hospital, they escorted me to a room. I was made comfortable in a hospital gown and positioned in bed to await the doctor. Tommy was a bundle of nerves and unsure of what to do with himself.

A short time later, a nurse came in. "Mr. Serino, Dr. Perino called and asked if you could come to his house and pick him up. His car won't start."

"Oh my gosh. He's not even in the hospital yet?" Tommy exclaimed. He then left to retrieve the doctor.

After examining me, Dr. Perino said, "Well, it's going to be a little while yet. The nurse will come and get me when it's time to go to the delivery room. I'll be here in the hospital, Mr. Serino. Don't worry." That was around five in the morning.

The baby didn't arrive until 2:24 in the afternoon—a beautiful baby boy weighing eight pounds and six ounces. We named him Thomas.

There were no restrictions on visitations, so all the family from Poughkeepsie came to visit: both sets of grandparents, Aunt Kay, Uncle Jerry, Aunt Dolores and Uncle Johnny, Aunt Betty, Aunt Tessie and Uncle Mike, and everyone else who was local. My family from New Windsor came to visit at my mother's house after we left the hospital.

Following a five-day stay in the hospital, I was discharged in good condition with a healthy little boy. We came home to everything ready for a new baby. I had the bassinette in our room and was prepared for nighttime feedings every two hours. Life with a new baby was a major adjustment. Bottles had to be boiled and cooled, a job that was done several times each day. Milk was warmed on the stove, and diapers had to be washed daily.

One month later when Little Tommy had his first immunizations, he was inconsolable. He cried all day long and into the evening. He wouldn't let me sit down. I had to pace the floor with him, and my back was killing me. Tom was across the street at the candy store playing cards and I had no way to contact him, so for hours I had no relief.

When Tom came home, I lashed out at him. He was gracious and took the baby and put both of us to bed. I assumed the responsibility of nighttime care myself. I didn't wake Tom because his job required him to work on scaffolds and I was afraid if he didn't have sufficient sleep, he might fall. There were nights when I would fall asleep with the baby in my arms and Tom would find the two of us sleeping peacefully together on the couch.

We had many visitors in the first few months. Friends and family would stop over to see the baby and offer congratulations. Little Tommy grew strong and healthy. He was a big baby and very intelligent. He started talking at six months old, and by one year old he was speaking in full sentences. He began to walk with the assistance of a walker at six months old and was walking on his own three months later. Then the summer of 1957 saw an epidemic of the Asian flu, and Little Tommy was an unfortunate participant. At first the flu symptoms were mild, so I covered his crib and placed the vaporizer inside to facilitate his breathing. But his symptoms worsened. He wasn't sleeping, and he had diarrhea, stomach cramps, and high fever, so the pediatrician, Dr. Koloski, treated him with antibiotics. He also suggested putting a drop of whiskey in Little Tommy's bottle to help him sleep. "And I suggest that you take a shot yourself," the doctor advised me.

It seemed that Little Tommy never fully recovered from the Asian flu. Over the next few months, he looked pale and weak. His energy level was low, and he was constantly fatigued. At his first birthday party, he showed little interest in cake or presents. He had no interest in playing with his cousins and napped for a large part of the afternoon.

In December we were to spend Christmas with my parents, and everyone was anticipating the holiday with high hopes. This was Little Tommy's first Christmas that he could participate —he'd been only a month old the year before—but he slept late that morning, and it was necessary to wake him to open his gifts. Tom and I were excited to share the magic of Christmas with Little Tommy and to see the holiday through the eyes of a small child, but he was detached, unconcerned, and merely wanted to be held.

We went to my parents' house for dinner, and there were more toys and a plethora of activities, but Little Tommy was disengaged and indifferent to everyone and everything. He had received a toy piano complete with a bench as a Christmas gift, and with him dressed in a tiny suit, we sat him on the bench at the piano to take a photo. Later we saw how pale and sickly he looked in the photo. We went home early, fed Little Tommy a bottle, and put him to bed.

Two days after Christmas, Tom and I went to look at a house for sale and left Little Tommy with my mother. When we returned home, she was extremely upset. "Something is wrong with this baby, Doris. I tried to stand him up and he just collapsed on the floor."

So we rushed him to Dr. Koloski's office, and after a brief examination the doctor sent us to the pediatric ward at Saint Francis Hospital. We had no idea how sick our baby was.

Little Tommy was admitted and had several vials of blood drawn. The doctor ordered a rush on the blood tests so he could quickly determine the necessary treatment. Tom and I waited for what seemed an inordinate amount of time in the waiting room while our baby was subjected to every imaginable examination.

When we were permitted to enter his room, Little Tommy was asleep. He had IV in his right arm, and a monitor resembling a radio was recording some pertinent information. He looked so pale, his skin was the color of the sheet. I couldn't understand how he could be so ill and we could be so oblivious. While we waited for the doctor, I stroked Little Tommy's hair and whispered how much I loved him. Tom sat in a chair in shocked disbelief.

Finally, the doctor escorted us to a private room for consultation. I was certain that this was not going to be good news. "Mr. and Mrs. Serino let's talk about your baby's condition," he began. "I will tell you now that he is in critical condition. We have done extensive blood tests, and thankfully they have ruled out leukemia. But your child is severely anemic. I'm waiting for the results from one more test to confirm my suspicions, but the electrophoresis can take up to twenty-four hours. Tonight, unfortunately, there is nothing more we can do but keep Little Tommy comfortable. We're treating him with antibiotics to prevent secondary infection and keeping him hydrated. I've ordered blood and it's being matched as we speak. I suggest that you go home and get a good night's rest and come back in the morning. We should have more information for you then. Do you have any questions?"

That was far too much for me to absorb. Overwhelmed, I only wanted to know one thing. "Is he going to be all right, doctor?"

Dr. Koloski looked at me seriously but with great compassion. "I won't lie to you, Mrs. Serino. He's in a very serious state. How he fares through the night is vital. There's nothing you can do here, so get some rest, and we'll call you if there is any change."

I desperately wanted to stay. The thought of leaving my baby alone in the hospital was devastating, but the hospital didn't allow parents to remain with their children overnight, saying it could potentially hinder the child's treatment. So Tom and I reluctantly left the hospital and spent a sleepless night of dread and worry waiting for a phone call that we hoped would never come. That was the first time I'd ever seen Tom cry. We wept openly from fear and sorrow and passed the endless night together.

Sunrise found us both awake. I had made coffee, but neither of us were hungry. We each took our turn in the bathroom and then left for the hospital. We were able to see Little Tommy right away. He was asleep and still looked as pale and fragile as he had the previous night.

Dr. Koloski was there, having spent the night at the hospital. He greeted us with slightly more optimism than yesterday. "Mr. and Mrs. Serino, good morning. Thankfully, Little Tommy is still with us. Unfortunately, there is little change in his condition. I received the results of the electrophoresis late last night and they confirmed my suspicions. Your son is suffering from Mediterranean anemia. It's a genetic disorder found in people of Mediterranean descent—Italians, Greeks, and Syrians primarily. It's characterized by decreased hemoglobin production. Either too little hemoglobin or, more likely, the hemoglobin is missing a component that enables it to carry oxygen. Either way, the treatment is the same. We can do blood transfusions, but this I will only do if absolutely necessary. Too many blood transfusions can result in iron overload and cause damage to the heart, liver, and endocrine system. I prefer to treat your son with an elixir to supplement his iron deficiency, and a high-protein diet. We'll begin this regimen today and see how he responds."

I spent all day every day at the hospital with Little Tommy in my arms. I was so grateful to have my baby alive and responding to treatment. He began to recover almost immediately when the treatment began, and although it was a gradual recovery, the doctor was encouraged by how well the baby reacted to the high-protein diet and the elixir.

After about ten days, Little Tommy became quite

animated and it was more difficult to administer the elixir, which evidently had a nasty taste. At the two-week mark, Dr. Koloski entered the room with a concerned look on his face. "I'm going to discharge the baby today, Mrs. Serino. I don't want to do this, as I believe it to be premature, but there's an outbreak of the flu in the city and the pediatric ward is overflowing with flu cases. I want to send you home before your son falls victim to this outbreak."

I now understood why I was told not to take Little Tommy out of his hospital room several days ago. The doctor was concerned that Little Tommy was still too weak to survive the flu, so he was discharged within the hour and the doctor gave me specific instructions on his treatment.

We had been home only one day when Little Tommy came down with the flu. Dr. Koloski refused to admit him to the hospital, believing he could better treat Tommy with antibiotics while isolated at home. He was correct. Tommy recovered from the flu quickly, and we were able to continue his treatment for Mediterranean anemia at home unabated.

Tommy's daily regimen consisted of a diet high in protein: two eggs, cheese, and hamburger. He was also required to take an iron supplement daily for two years. He didn't like that. He would fight and scream and cry, but it was important to augment the deficiency in his blood. His blood was monitored regularly for iron content, and he never needed a blood transfusion.

While Little Tommy was looking better, and his color and activity level returned to normal, there would be some lasting effects he would experience as he matured. Minor bone deformities in both of his hands caused his fingers to grow slightly crooked, and he experienced a much slower growth rate, resulting in his adult height being a full six inches less than predicted. He also had a late introduction to puberty, not experiencing full pubescence until he was in his mid-teens. Apart from these effects, he grew strong and healthy and lived to be a father and grandfather.

By the end of January, Little Tommy's treatment was advancing well, and it was certain that he would make a full recovery. I would sit him in front of the television to watch *Howdy Doody* or *American Bandstand* while I fed him. He would be so mesmerized by the puppets and the music and dancing that feeding him was easy. Giving the elixir was another story, and I couldn't blame him. The elixir had the most pungent aroma and repulsive taste of any medicine I had encountered. As soon as he saw the bottle, he would begin to cry. He was growing stronger, so the struggle was real.

We were now accustomed to life with a toddler needing special care, but it did take all our effort. There was little time for anything other than general household chores and seeing to the needs of our baby. It was clear to us that we certainly couldn't handle anything more.

And then I became pregnant with our second baby.

TWENTY-TWO
Second Child

"A re you certain, Dr. Perino?" I asked after a moment of speechlessness.

"Yes, Mrs. Serino. You are pregnant," the doctor confirmed.

I was surprised and a little concerned about having an infant while my toddler was still recovering from a life-threatening illness. I had developed a workable routine for Tommy's care, and now that I was just feeling comfortable balancing that and my household chores, I was learning that I was pregnant again.

Tom and I were very happy with the news, but we were also nervous. Just months before, we had nearly lost our first child to a genetic disorder. What were the chances of this occurring again? How would I function, caring for Tommy and a newborn? These questions were on our hearts when we met with the doctor for the first prenatal visit.

Dr. Perino was very comforting and helped to put our minds at rest. He explained that while there was a possibility that any children we had would show symptoms of

Mediterranean anemia, the chance a second child would experience a full-blown onset of the disease was small. Dr. Koloski, our pediatrician, concurred with the obstetrician, saying we should take comfort in how well Tommy responded to treatment. So, armed with the reassurance of the doctors, we began to prepare for the arrival of our second child.

We were now in a new apartment, having moved farther uptown to North Clinton Street when Tommy was eight months old. Union Street, where I had grown up, was not the same, and Tom had a heightening concern over the changing state of our neighborhood. IBM had moved into our area and hired many returning veterans, providing good salaries, so more people were able to purchase a house. The suburbs were a growing phenomenon around the nation.

Until this time, people either lived in a city or on a farm. Outside the city limits, the area was completely rural. Surrounding the city of Poughkeepsie were small family farms, numerous orchards, and a few large dairy farms. There were also acres of natural forests, meadows, and fields. These were purchased by land developers who built entire neighborhoods of single-family houses at affordable prices. It was the beginning of a large-scale exodus of families from the city to suburban life.

As families prospered, they moved from the city to pursue this new lifestyle, leaving a poorer class of people remaining. Between our building and Dietrich and Martin's meat market next door was a small alley. There was a bar on Main Street, and men would frequently leave the bar and cut through the alley. They would often urinate there or break bottles of booze, resulting in a stench that prevented us from opening our windows during the summer.

One night two colored men had a fight on Union Street, directly in front of our apartment. It was so violent with punching and shouting, I was terrified. Tom said, "That's it. That's the last straw. We're moving out of here the first chance we get." So in July 1957, we moved to 147 North Clinton Street.

That summer I also obtained my driver's license. Tom was not a patient teacher. He was entirely too nervous, and we frequently ended the driving lesson with a fight. Nevertheless, I persevered and was able to pass my driver's test with no problem. Having my driver's license made it convenient for me to drive to visit my parents' house rather than take the bus with a toddler, and it proved to be essential in the spring of 1958.

I now had frequent doctor visits between Tommy's check-ups with the pediatrician and my obstetric appointments with Dr. Perino. Obtaining evening doctor visits became more and more difficult, so when I needed to see the doctor, I would awaken early in the morning, make Tom's breakfast and fix his lunch, then feed Tommy and dress him so we could take Tom to work. Thankfully, sometimes Tom was able to hitch a ride with another laborer, freeing me of the responsibility of dropping him off and picking him up later.

My second pregnancy was uneventful. The only problem I encountered was that I gained a lot of weight, even more than with my first pregnancy. The extra sixty pounds made life difficult for a tiny woman under five feet tall. We lived on the second floor, so negotiating the stairs was perilous when I couldn't see my feet. I was as big as a house, and caring for an active toddler who could outrun me proved to be complicated.

In the early morning hours of October 2, I awoke in great discomfort. I went to the kitchen to get a drink, and suddenly my water broke. There was a tremendous amount of fluid, which frightened me, so I woke Tom up and he mopped up the floor while I called the doctor. We left for the hospital at four in the morning.

When I entered the labor and delivery room, the nurse commented to the doctor, "Her water broke and there's no fluid remaining, but her stomach is still extremely large. Do you think that she's carrying twins?"

"I only hear one heartbeat," the doctor said, "but it is possible that a second baby is behind the first one."

I was sent to X-ray while in active labor, which confirmed that there was only one—very large—baby.

"I told you this might happen, Doris," the doctor chided. "It looks like you'll need a cesarean section. You barely delivered the first baby, and this one is much larger."

But Dr. Perino didn't do C-sections. He had a partner, Dr. Basile, who performed all sections. Since it would take some time for him to arrive and prepare for delivery, Dr. Perino said, "Let's wait a while, Doris, and see what develops. I'd like you to be able to deliver naturally if possible."

I labored for hours, and the pains increased greatly. Soon they became unbearable, and I told the doctor, "Dr. Perino, I can't handle this any longer." So, on the morning of October 3, after a long night of labor, they brought me into the delivery room and performed the cesarean section.

When our second son was born, the cord was around his neck and he wasn't breathing. The staff tried everything to stimulate his breathing, but nothing was working. Finally, they decided to shock him by dunking him in hot water and then in cold water. After doing this several times, the baby began to cry. He hadn't breathed for so long, and the exposure to the water treatment complicated his condition, so the medical staff were concerned for his survival. The priest was called, and he baptized the baby.

"What is the baby's name, Mrs. Serino?" the nurse asked so the priest could perform the baptism.

"His name is Joseph, after my father," I said. Then my blood pressure dropped dramatically and I went into shock. Both my baby and I were now in critical condition.

The nursing staff wouldn't let me see the baby at first. When I asked to see him, they said, "We can't, Mrs. Serino. The baby is in the incubator. We've been treating him for hypothermia."

Several days passed, and I insisted on seeing Joey. I thought he had died since I'd seen the priest in the delivery room. When they finally brought the baby to me, I was relieved to see him alive and well, and surprised at how big he was. We stayed two more weeks in the hospital, both of us needing every moment to regain our strength.

In the meantime, my sister, Kay, had met a wonderful man named Ray MacDermott at Domestic Finance, where they both worked. They were to be married on November 2, one month after Joey's birth. After almost two weeks in the hospital, I told the nurse, "I have to go home. My sister is getting married in two weeks and I'm the maid of honor."

"I'm sorry, but you can't go yet, honey," the nurse said gently.

I begged Dr. Perino, and he finally relented and permitted me to be discharged, but with strict orders to "take it easy." Fortunately, Kay had been a bridesmaid in a wedding the month before, so she had her gown shortened and Ray's mother altered it to fit me. Two weeks after leaving the hospital, I attended my sister's wedding to a man with whom she would be married for over fifty years. Life is a series of adjustments, and with each new child certain rearrangements need to be made. I had an active medically complex toddler whose specialized treatment took great effort to maintain. I had a husband and a household to care for, which accounted for the rest of my energy. And now we had added an infant to my list of responsibilities, which required additional bottles, diapers, and laundry, as well as midnight feedings, doctor visits, and general oversight of the welfare of another tiny human being. I had truly reached my limit. There was nothing more I could endure, or so I thought.

I took the boys to Dr. Koloski for Joey's one-month-old well check-up. As we sat in the waiting room, Tommy was "reading" the *Highlights for Children* magazine and Joey was asleep in my arms. "Mommy," Tommy said, "can I have a piece of gum, please?"

"Here, baby. Put the paper in the garbage can over there," I instructed.

A woman watched Tommy take the gum from the wrapper and deposit the paper in the waste can, then take his seat and continue to peruse the magazine. "Won't he swallow that?" she asked with concern.

"No," I replied. "He'll chew it until it has no flavor, then he'll put it in the trash."

"How old is he?" the woman asked.

"Two years old."

"My, he's very intelligent, isn't he?" the woman commented.

"Yes, we are very thankful," I answered.

Joey's appointment went as expected. The doctor

checked his vitals and commented that his growth was excellent. He was responsive and alert and all looked good. Then with a more serious demeanor, he said, "I'd like to show you something, Mrs. Serino." He laid the baby on his back and moved his leg in various directions. "Do you see the hip as I move his leg?"

It seemed like an odd question, and I couldn't understand what the doctor was demonstrating.

"Here, place your hand on Joey's hip while I move his leg," the doctor said. As he rotated the leg, I felt it move apart from the hip as if it was separating from his body.

"Mrs. Serino, I'm afraid your baby has a congenital dislocation."

I swallowed. "What does that mean, doctor?"

"The hip joint is supposed to be rounded, and like a ball and socket the leg rotates within the hip. But your baby's hip is straight, rather than rounded, so that the top of his leg does not fit into the joint."

"What can be done to fix it, doctor?" I asked.

"I'm recommending that you see the orthopedic doctor, Dr. Ettenson, on the first floor of this building. He'll be able to prescribe the best treatment. I will tell you, Mrs. Serino, that the condition is serious, but it is completely curable with proper treatment."

And so, when I thought I could endure no more, life gave me an opportunity to grow stronger through yet another trial.

We took Joey to Dr. Ettenson, and he prescribed a Frejka splint for him. It was a most unusual contraption, with a large pillow strapped between Joey's legs to keep them spread completely apart. His legs were never to come together until the treatment period was finished and the hip socket had been corrected.

This presented a tremendous problem with bathing and changing Joey's diaper. How was I to keep his legs apart and successfully change him without compromising the hip joint? When Tom was home, he was able to hold Joey's legs apart while I changed him, but what was I to do when Tom was at work?

One evening my father came over to our apartment with a gift.

"Hi, Daddy," I greeted him. "What have you got?"

"I brought something for the baby, Dolly." It was a piece of wood, shaped like a crescent moon with straps on it, that had been sanded and varnished to ensure protection against water. "It's for changing little Joey." He placed the apparatus on the kitchen table. "When you're going to change him, place him here on his back in the center of the wood. Then when you take off the pillow, strap his legs to either side of the device and it will keep his legs apart while you change him. It's treated so you can clean it when you're finished."

I was overwhelmed with joy and affection. My father had designed an invention that made changing my baby safe and efficient. I gave him a huge hug and tearfully said, "Thank you, Daddy. You're my hero."

My dad kissed my cheek. "Now, where are my little grandsons?"

As Joey grew, the brace grew with him. In the beginning he wore a six-inch pillow. He soon graduated to a nine inch, then a twelve-inch pillow. Since he was unable to crawl, he pulled himself around the floor and developed excellent upper body strength and coordination. He wore the Frejka splint for two years, after which Dr. Ettenson declared him completely cured.

Joey began to walk not long after the Frejka splint was

removed, and soon he was toddling after his older brother. He had several follow-up visits with Dr. Ettenson after the brace was removed to ensure that he was walking correctly. Right before the second follow-up visit, I noticed the same leg that had the congenital dislocation was beginning to bow dramatically. Joey was walking with a limp and seemed uncomfortable when he stepped forward. So I took him to the doctor before his regular follow-up.

Dr. Ettenson took X-rays and discovered that Joey had developed leg perthes, which was a softening of the head of the femur due to temporary lack of blood flow to the bone. "But, Doctor, I thought that you said he was cured," I said.

"I did, Mrs. Serino. This condition has nothing to do with the former congenital dislocation."

"Then why is it happening again in the same leg, at the same joint?"

He shook his head. "I don't know for certain, but I have a theory. You may recall that Joey had the flu in February."

That was true. He had been quite sick with the flu, and throughout the month of March he continued to run a low-grade fever, between 100 and 100.2 degrees. The doctor's theory was that the flu virus remained dormant in Joey and found the weakest spot in his body and exploited the blood supply, thus cutting off the blood flow to the area temporarily. This seemed to make sense since Joey had been walking perfectly before contracting the flu and I noticed his limping and bowing leg in April.

So, at the age of two years and six months, Joey began using crutches for the first time. It was a difficult adjustment for him, and Tom made a harness for him to support his damaged leg. Joey would use crutches for many years before he was able to walk without them. Dr. Ettenson made the journey with us through all those years and was able to bring Joey to a place of independent mobility without surgery.

As the years passed, Tom and I were careful not to favor or overindulge Joey. He had his chores to do just like our other children. He learned to play baseball and kickball, and to run, sled, and play with equal fervor to others, and all while using crutches. When he went to school, I spoke with the teachers and administrators, instructing them that Joey was not accustomed to special measures and was to be treated in the same manner as other children. The school respected our concerns, and Joey did everything that was required of all students. As a result, he grew up well adjusted, never feeling sorry for himself, never being excluded. He wanted to do what everyone else was doing, and he did.

Eventually, Joey was able to walk without the aid of crutches. He grew to be a fine man, father, and grandfather. Sadly, he continued to have chronic pain in his hip that endured throughout his life, but the resilience of those formative years created a heart of perseverance that enabled him to press on.

The winter of 1958–1959 was very cold, and the apartment on North Clinton Street gave little protection against the elements. In the summer we sweltered in the heat and humidity, longing for a breath of air to be carried through our second-floor windows. Now we were freezing, bundling the babies, and placing hot water bottles in their cribs, while Tom and I shivered under the covers in our bed. We had two stoves going in the apartment—the gas stove in the living room and the oil stove in the kitchen. It was so cold that condensation would run down the walls.

The boys had the bedroom right off ours. I would dress Tommy in heavy pajamas and wrap him in blankets. It was easier to wrap Joey up because he had the Dennis Brown bar for his legs, and he moved very little at night. Tom and I would go to bed in our pajamas, robes, and socks.

One night after we put the boys to bed and climbed under the layers of blankets, Tom turned to me and said, "We've got to find a place of our own. Renting is too uncertain. How many times have we complained to the landlord about the cold in this apartment and still our babies are shivering in their beds."

"Don't worry, Tom," I said. "Something will materialize for us. It always does."

TWENTY-THREE
Our Final Move

I t was a damp, foggy morning in March, and the drizzling rain was all that remained from the downpour the night before. Yet the dampness seemed to permeate the walls of the apartment making everything feel colder than the actual temperature. Having endured the bitter cold winter, we were now experiencing the chill of the spring rains. I was cooking Tom's breakfast when he entered the kitchen, fastening the last buttons on his flannel shirt.

"Is that shirt going to be warm enough for you?" I asked.

"It'll be fine," he said. "I have my long johns on underneath."

"I have a full thermos of coffee for you, and for your lunch a thermos of steaming chicken soup."

Tom smiled, came to the stove where I was busy frying eggs, and put his arms around me. "You take such good care of me."

I grinned. "I don't want my honey getting cold out there today. It's such miserable weather."

Tom sat down at the table, and I served his breakfast, then sat across from him and sipped my coffee. We sat silently for a few moments before he looked up with a sad expression on his face. "I hate leaving you and the boys here in this cold apartment."

"It's really not bad," I told him. "I need to boil the baby's bottles, and that always warms the kitchen nicely."

Tom continued, seeming to have something on his mind this morning. "You know, we froze here all winter, and now the rain is bringing a soggy coldness right inside."

"Well, if it's any consolation, summer will be here soon and we'll be sweltering again," I said, attempting a little levity.

"I'm serious, Doris, we have to get out of here," he replied, obviously not in the mood for humor. "We suffocate in the summer heat, and we freeze with the brutal arctic winds all winter."

"Well, what can we do, Tommy? There are no available apartments in town, and besides, most of the places we can afford are no better than this one."

"That's my point. We need a place of our own," Tom determined.

I sighed. "We've been over this many times now. What can we do? We have no money for a down payment. No bank will give us a mortgage. We really don't have any options." I knew this was painful for Tom to hear. He worked so hard to provide for us, but the reality was that opportunities were few and buying a house was out of the question at this point in our lives.

"Well, something has got to change," Tom said.

I went to my frustrated husband, put my arms around him, and kissed his cheek. "It will. I know it will. And as long as I have you near me, the house is warm enough.

Now, you'd better get going or you'll be late for work. It's a long ride to that school you're working on, you know."

"It's only a few miles away. I'll be there on time." He got up and went to get his coat.

At the front door, he kissed me goodbye and was gone.

At that time, Tom was doing the brick work on a new school in Red Oaks Mill, about six miles outside of Pough-keepsie. He was nearing the end of that job, but we were hoping it would continue through the springtime—until the summer months brought more job opportunities. I had just put Joey down for his afternoon nap and Tommy was watching Bozo the Clown on the television when the phone rang.

"Hello?" I said after picking up the receiver.

"Hi, Doris. It's Dolores."

"Oh. Hi, Dolores. What's up?" I was surprised to hear from her. Dolores was not one for talking on the phone, especially with two little girls, as well as Jerry's two children, to watch.

"Hey, Doris, is Tommy home yet?"

"Not yet. He won't be home until about four this after-noon. Why?"

"Well, Johnny just called. He wants to come over and talk to Tommy about something. I don't know what it's about, but Johnny was pretty excited."

"Okay. Well, Tommy will be home by four, so if he wants to, Johnny can come over any time after that."

"All right. Thanks, Doris. Kiss the boys for me. Bye."

Later that afternoon, Tom was sitting at the kitchen table when Johnny arrived. As soon as they both had a cup of coffee, Johnny shared his news. "You know the school where you're working, out on Vassar Road, right? Well, the property directly across from the school is for sale."

"How do you know this?" Tom asked.

"Because the real estate agency I work for is listing the property. It's just over one acre of land, and they're selling it for eleven hundred dollars. I spoke to my boss about it and told him that you would be interested in seeing it."

I walked over to the table. "Johnny, you know we can't afford to buy that property. It may as well be a million dollars."

But Johnny was undeterred. "Look, tomorrow is Saturday. How about we take a ride out and look at the place? It doesn't cost anything to look."

Tom hesitated for a moment, then said, "All right, let's do it."

The next morning Johnny was at our apartment by nine o'clock. I was feeding the boys breakfast and Tom was getting dressed. "There's my little nephews," Johnny said as he entered the kitchen.

"Hi, Uncle Johnny," Tommy said. "You gonna get us a house?"

"I hope so, buddy," Johnny said optimistically.

I wasn't so certain, and Johnny could obviously tell. "Don't worry, Doris, I really think this is going to work for you guys," he said.

"I just don't want to see Tom disappointed again," I replied. "He's had enough disappointment in his life."

Tom entered the room. "You ready, Johnny?"

"All set."

Turning to me, Tom said, "We'll be back soon."

After they were gone, Tommy looked at me. "Mommy, is Daddy going to buy us a house?"

"I hope so, baby," I replied. "I hope so."

About two hours later, Tom and Johnny returned. Johnny didn't stay since his parents were coming over that afternoon, but Tom came into the house bursting with excitement. "The place is perfect," he said. "Can your mother watch the boys for a bit? I want you to see the property."

So we dropped the boys off to my mother after lunch and Tom and I took the drive to Vassar Road to see the lot. The drive was longer than I expected. We pulled on to an old dirt road past a large colonial farmhouse and drove a short distance to the end. I could see the school building that was being erected and the construction site, and Tom said that the shanty for the workers was on the property we were considering. We walked around the land, which had a slight incline and was surrounded by trees. There was another empty lot next to the property and a house after the lot.

Tom said that a family named Ostrander lived there. He was the one selling the land. All the property around had been owned by his father, and when the man passed away, the family sold the land to the school district and kept three lots for the three sons. Two of the sons had since moved out of state, and Bob Ostrander was now selling one of the lots and keeping the one next to his house. I could see the hope in Tom's eyes as he walked around the land, explaining how he would build us a house and what it would look like. I wanted to fantasize about this land as ours, but I knew the financial reality was bound to bring dismay.

On the drive home I was quiet, so Tom asked, "Well, what do you think?"

I took a deep breath before answering, not wanting to crush my enthusiastic husband's dreams. "Well, the property is beautiful. We couldn't ask for a better place. It's perfect for the boys," I began. "But, Tommy, what about the cost? Where are we going to get eleven hundred dollars to buy the land? Even then, what bank will give us a mortgage to build a house?"

Tom was not dissuaded. "Don't worry, Doris. Johnny has spoken to his boss and his company is going to help us to get the mortgage."

I was shocked. I wasn't ready to believe that this could be a possibility. "How?" was all I could say.

"Johnny's coming over on Monday night with a signed receipt stating that the property is paid in full. We're to take that to the bank when applying for the mortgage so the bank will see that we own a property on which to build a house. Then, when they give us the loan, we'll pay the real estate agency for the land."

I was speechless. This might actually work. I was ready to be excited, but we still had to convince a bank to loan us the money to build a house.

So, Monday afternoon Tom came home from work early and we drove to Banker's Trust to apply for a mortgage. We spoke to the mortgage loan originator, filled out all the necessary paperwork, provided the financial information, and left in high hopes. Two days later we received notification that our mortgage application had been declined.

We were disappointed but not discouraged. We regrouped, gathered every piece of positive financial information we could find, and headed to Poughkeepsie Savings Bank. Kay had loaned us $800 she had been saving, and we brought some bonds that we had as additional collateral. Whether it was because of our youthful optimism or our honest approach or just the hope on our faces, the bank approved us for ten thousand dollars on a twenty-year loan. There was one condition before we could receive the money: although we were approved, we would receive no cash until forty percent of the house was built. This was yet another enigma. How could we obtain the building materials to build forty percent of the house without any money?

The next morning Tom had a very important stop to make on his way to work. "What's the worst they can say, Doris, 'No, you can't have the materials'? I have to try," Tom declared. He was on his way to Fairview Block Company to request the purchase of a load of block without cash. His request for deferred payment on construction materials was not unusual for construction companies or contractors, but for private individuals it was unprecedented.

Tom knew the people at Fairview since he had dealt with them on many occasions over the years as a bricklayer. He was hoping this relationship would be enough to warrant his request. Tom hoped to start with this business and get a favorable outcome so he could communicate Fairview's willingness to help, with the lumber and cement companies and hopefully have a similar result.

"Okay, honey," I said brimming with optimism. "You just show them your charming face. How could they say no to you? I couldn't."

He smiled and kissed me as he walked out the door. "Wish me luck," were his departing words.

Tom returned later that afternoon, ecstatic with joy. Fairview Block Company had approved all the concrete masonry units he needed to begin the project, with delayed payments until midsummer. We were incredulous at how things were falling into place. Now Tom was ready to approach the lumber yard, armed with the information that a reputable business such as Fairview Block Company was willing to defer payments.

He went to the Fishkill Landing Company and spoke with the son of the owner. "We've been approved for a mortgage through Poughkeepsie Savings Bank," Tom began, showing the man the affidavit from the bank as proof, "but we won't receive any release of funds until forty percent of the house is built. If you give us the needed materials, we'll pay you in full when we receive our first payment from the bank."

The owner's son was not convinced of the wisdom of loaning such a large amount of resources to someone with only the promise of future assets. "Okay, why don't you wait here, Mr. Serino," he said. "I need to speak with my father concerning this matter."

As the young man left the office, Tom felt a twinge of fear grip him and a cold chill surge through him. The young man entered the adjoining office where an older, gray-haired gentleman sat behind a desk. "Dad, I have a situation here I want to share with you." The young man explained the circumstances to his father, who listened carefully.

"So, he has no cash, but he has a mortgage that will pay him when forty percent of the house is built, is that correct?" the father clarified.

"Yes," the young man confirmed.

"Give him what he needs," replied the father confidently. "He's an honest man."

Tom received this favorable treatment from the block company, the lumber company, the cement company, and the excavator. Miraculously, we had everything we needed to begin building our home, and all without any cash in hand.

We purchased the lot in April, and Tom began work on the house immediately. At first it was convenient since he

TOM SERINO

was doing masonry work at the school. When the workday
was finished, he would simply walk to the adjoining property, now belonging to us, to labor on the house. He had the
excavation for the foundation done on a Saturday, then
Tom began the block work so the floor could be poured on
the following Saturday. He spent the afternoon floating and
troweling the concrete so the foundation floor would be
perfect. Tom then continued the block work to complete
what would become a basement and laundry area.

Unfortunately, soon after he began working on the
house, the job at the school ended. There was another
union job available immediately, but it was in Connecticut,
almost an hour away. Tom was in no position to turn the
job down, so at the start of the third week in April, Tom
began a routine that would continue through the entire
summer. He would drive to Connecticut to work each
morning, then at the end of the workday, he would hurry
home, eat his dinner, and drive out to work on the house
until the sun went down. He would then come home,
shower, and drop into bed exhausted.

Every night Tom went to work on the house. On Saturdays he was there from early morning until sundown. On
Sundays he would go to early mass, then work on the house
for the remainder of the day. He wasn't alone on the weekends. Kay's husband, Ray, and my father assisted him. On
weekdays during the summer, when the days were long and
the sun didn't set until nine at night, Daddy and Ray would
often help Tom after work.

These two wonderful men were the only family that
helped through the entire process. Although Pop Serino was
a contractor, he never once offered any help to Tom in
building the house. Tom resented this, and it drove the
wedge deeper into their relationship. Sometimes I would

pack a picnic lunch and take the boys out to the house while Tom was there. They were excited to see Daddy working on their house and enjoyed seeing Grandpa and Uncle Ray.

Once the foundation was complete, Tom called and had the lumber and supplies delivered. He began working to frame the house, and it was thrilling to see the future home of the Serino family taking shape. This was a stressful time for us, and it caused some strain. One weekend when they were nailing the plywood to the rafters, I heard Tom shouting at my father. When he was working, Tom had very little patience and would often bark commands like an overseer on a plantation.

I was furious that Tom would speak in that manner to my father, especially when he was there to help him. When the men came down for lunch, I said to my father, "Daddy, why do you put up with him when he yells like that? If he yelled at me like that I'd say, 'To hell with you. Do it yourself,' then I'd leave."

My wise and patient father simply replied, "Oh, he doesn't mean anything by it. He's under a lot of pressure and he's just letting off steam."

This pressure ultimately did cause a rift in the Serino family. Tom had done a favor for his brother-in-law, Johnny, and in return, Johnny had promised to come out and assist Tom with something at the house. I don't know what it was, something about the fireplace, quite insignificant in the large scheme of things. But Johnny promised he would come out that Saturday and never did. Tom waited for him, and by the end of the day he was furious. He had lost a full day's worth of work.

The next time he saw Johnny, they argued furiously, each saying hurtful things and then retreating to neutral corners. Tom's reaction was very strong, fueled in part by his resentment toward his family because they'd offered no help at a time when he needed it most. He considered Johnny's failure to appear when he had committed to doing so, as a personal affront to him.

As angry as Tom was with his brother-in-law over this incident, it would have blown over in a few weeks had it not been for the interference of Tom's mother. She inserted herself into the situation, accusing Tom of being unreasonable and childish and insisting that he go and apologize to Johnny.

"For what?" Tom responded. "He promised to be there, and he didn't show up."

Mom Serino continued to badger Tom, demanding that he apologize to Johnny, and the more she pressed him, the more obstinate Tom became. The result was that this incident, which would have swiftly dissipated into memory, became a wall of separation between Tom and Johnny for more than two decades.

Once the house was framed and the wall sheathing was in place, the roof was finished and the brickwork was begun, we went to the bank to report our progress. The bank sent an adjuster to inspect the work. We then received the promised forty percent of our loan, four thousand dollars. I opened a separate checking account designated for the house expenses, and we paid the real estate company, Fairview Block Company, Fishkill Landing Company, and the rest of the businesses that had fronted the building materials to us. The rest of the construction, the plumber, electrician, the septic, etc., was paid for as the work was completed.

One of the final stages in building the house was plastering the walls. This was done by Kenny Thompson, a friend of Tom who he had met through the union. Kenny was older, but they'd become great friends. They would often leave the union meetings together and stop for ice cream, and after we moved into the house, Kenny and his wife, Amy, would visit once a week and they always brought ice cream.

With the plastering completed, Tom began the finishing work inside: building closets, hanging doors, installing hardwood flooring, finishing the bathroom, and connecting appliances. Everything was completed by the end of October. Tom had built our home in just six months.

As the summer ended and the coolness of autumn was upon us, Tom was finishing the last of the inside work on the house. I began moving in everything that was not necessary for daily apartment living. I hung curtains and brought small accessories. As the closets were completed, I brought clothes to fill them. And once my kitchen was ready, I brought my dishes and began filling the pantry. I accomplished so much that on moving day, I had only one wine barrel filled with household items to unpack.

The bank gave us the remainder of the loan in two additional installments. We initiated monthly mortgage payments starting on November 1, the day after we moved in. That first year, our monthly mortgage payment was one hundred and seven dollars. Everything was ready: the house was ready, the truck was ready, the helpers—Ray and my father—were ready, and moving day was set for October 31, 1959.

The day before we moved, Kay had her second daughter. She was in the hospital, but Ray still came to help us move. It was pouring rain and there was no grass in the yard, so the property was awash with mud. They had to drive the truck around the back of the house to bring in our belongings. I had placed sheets on all the floors to protect the new tile and hardwood flooring.

We didn't own much in the way of furniture: a bed, two cribs, a couch, and a kitchen table with chairs. Our new neighbors, Bob and Tessie Ostrander, came over that night and helped us set up the beds and do a general cleanup. We had purchased bunkbeds for the boys, but they were too little yet—only three and one—so we kept them as single beds.

The boys were so cute when we brought them into the house for the first time and showed them their new bedroom. They ran and jumped onto the beds and giggled with delight. The sound of their laughter was an overture of joy welcoming us to a house we would call home for the rest of our lives.

Over the years, three more children came along, but we stayed in the same house. There were seven of us living in the house that Tom built, but we made it work for us. Tom lived for sixty-two years in this house, until he passed, and now that I'm alone, the house is still good for me.

TWENTY-FOUR

The Houseguest

The first few months in our new house were more of an adjustment than expected. The deafening silence of the nights caused sleep to elude the entire family. The boys were not able to settle and awoke at every sound in the rural darkness. Tom and I were accustomed to city noise—traffic, sirens, delivery trucks, and church bells—and the sounds of country living were subtle, prompting an eerie sensation with each strange reverberation. On cold nights when the heat turned on, the new floorboards would settle, making cracking noises simulating an intruder walking in the hallway.

My first attempt at laundering revealed a new dilemma. The washing machine was located in the basement, and the only access to the basement was through the Bilco doors in the back yard. Therefore, I had to carry my laundry out of the house into the back yard, open the Bilco doors, and descend the concrete stairs into the basement. When the snow arrived, this became a challenging mission. Tom was not able to construct an inside entry to the basement until springtime. So, washing clothes required a hat, coat, and boots until then.

Despite the modifications to our lifestyle, living in the country brought a tranquil beauty that transcended any momentary discomfort we may have experienced. One morning as I was preparing breakfast in the kitchen, I noticed Tom standing motionless in the living room. "What are you doing?" I asked.

"Shhhh," he whispered. "Come in here slowly."

I carefully walked into the next room, and he motioned toward the large picture window. To my amazement, there on the other side of the pane stood a colossal eight-point buck. He seemed undisturbed by our presence, his regal bearing emanating an aura that demanded homage. I was awestruck by his magnificence.

The smell of bacon on the threshold of charring broke the spell he'd cast over me, and I hurried to the kitchen to resume my household duties, but with a reverent appreciation of the splendor surrounding our new home.

The weekend arrived three days after moving day. It was a blessing to have Tom sleeping next to me rather than spending the entire day working on the house, as he had done for the last six months. Unfortunately, the boys were up bright and early, awakened by the sun shining through the bedroom window.

"Mommy, I'm hungry!" Tommy called from the next room, followed by Joey's tiny voice, "I hunky."

Tom drew me close in a warm embrace, and my desire to get up and see to my boys quickly dissipated.

"Mommy!" Tommy shouted indignantly.

Apparently, the decision had been made for me. I slowly climbed out of bed as Tom rolled over for a few more minutes of quietude.

The day progressed as any other weekend day. At midafternoon Tom was in the back yard clearing the residual construction debris, the boys were playing quietly on the living room floor, and I was busy reorganizing my kitchen cabinets. Suddenly, the sound of a loud, high-pitched engine came from the school parking lot next to our house. I hurried to the window, followed by Tommy, who scurried to the picture window. Joey, in the Frejka brace, hoisted himself up to peer over the windowsill. Tom, already standing in the front yard, motioned for us to join him outside.

I picked up Joey, took Tommy by the hand, and hastened out to join him. There in the school parking lot were two miniature race cars circling and jockeying for position, humming like giant bumble bees. As the boys squealed with delight, Tom and I smiled at each other and together we watched the display of their piloting prowess.

After a short time, the drivers pulled up next to our property and greeted us.

"Hi, there," Tom said.

Both young men exited their cars, took off their helmets, and came up to talk with us. "I hope we didn't disturb you," said the first driver.

"Not at all," Tom answered. "The boys are excited to watch you."

"Are you folks new here? We've been coming out some Saturdays recently and noticed the house going up. Are you all moved in now?"

"We moved in this past Wednesday," I volunteered.

"What do you do with these cars?" Tom asked.

"They're replicas of the Cooper Formula 3 racing cars, and we enter them in local auto races."

"Can I hold your helmet, mister?" Tommy asked.

"Sure, little man. Careful because it's heavy."

The first driver asked us, "Do you think the boys would like a ride? We'll just go around the circle a few times." Then looking at me, he added, "And we'll go nice and easy."

I was slightly nervous about the prospect of my babies whizzing around the parking lot at breakneck speed, but the boys were so excited, I couldn't refuse. So, Tom placed each boy in a race car and the driver got in next to them. The drivers attached the safety belts around the boys' laps and then they took off. We could hear the boys squealing and screeching. Joey was laughing and shouting, while Tommy was screaming, "It's too fast!"

The drivers circled the parking lot five or six times, then pulled up beside us again. Joey was still laughing, but Tommy exited the car, then turned to the driver and said, "You went too fast!"

Tom and I thanked the men and bid them goodbye, and they left. I was a little surprised, but we never saw them again after that day.

We continued settling into our new home. In the beginning of December, the circulator on our new furnace failed, and we were suddenly without heat and in immediate need of furnace repair. We discovered that the electricity in the area would often go out, so it was fortunate that we took the advice of our neighbor and installed a gas stove rather than an electric one. When the electricity failed, we were still able to cook and prepare bottles for the children.

Tom's big project that season was to plant grass seed in the front and back yards so in the springtime we would have a carpet of green lawn rather than the mud that surrounded the house. Our walls were newly plastered so we couldn't paint for a whole year. I always liked color, so I was anxious to decorate and finish the rooms.

One day while changing bed linens, I pulled a bed away from the wall to tuck in the sheet and was confronted with a wall mural in red crayon. Tommy, my miniature Michelangelo, had crawled under the bed and adorned the wall with pictures that mimicked cave drawings. He'd hidden his artistry so that until I moved the bed, it remained an undiscovered treasure. I scolded him and warned him not to do this again, especially when the walls were painted, but was a bit too late. Soon I discovered additional masterpieces on the closet wall board in blue crayon. Those designs I never painted over, and sixty-three years later they remain a faded testimony of the creativity of my oldest son.

We hosted our first Christmas in our house that year. Our neighbor Tessie knitted stockings for the boys with their names, and we hung them proudly on the mantel piece. My mother and father, Kay and Ray, and their two girls were all in attendance. As the years passed, we hosted many holidays with my parents and Kay, Ray, and their family, which grew to six children.

Mom Serino spent Christmas at Dolores and Johnny's house every year. She was already staying at Dolores's house since she had left Pop Serino for the umpteenth time. This had become a routine with her. She and Pop had nothing left of their marriage. He was out almost every night dallying with various women, while she occupied her time with friends. They lived separate lives under the same roof, and invariably there was conflict.

Whenever Mom got angry with Pop, she would leave him and stay with Dolores and Johnny until she was certain that he had been sufficiently punished. Then she would return to their apartment to continue their divided existence. This pattern continued for years. In December 1959, she left Pop again and stayed with Dolores's family for several weeks, through Christmas. It was during this time that Dolores had a stern talk with her.

"Ma, you can't keep doing this."

"Doing what?" Mom asked.

"You know exactly what I'm talking about. You can't keep leaving Daddy when you're angry and coming here until you cool off. This back and forth, leaving him and returning to him, has got to stop. Either you leave him and find an apartment for yourself, or you stay with him. You can't come back here anymore like this, Ma. It's too much stress on my family."

"Well, then maybe I should just jump off the Poughkeepsie bridge. Would you like that?" Mom chided.

"Look, Ma," Dolores said, ignoring her idle threats, "I can help you find an apartment if you want, but if you decide to go back to Daddy, you can't leave him again and expect to stay here. That's not going to happen any longer." Dolores was firm, and Mom understood.

After Christmas, Mom was at our house visiting when Pop called to speak with her. She refused to talk to him, so Pop asked me to give a message to her. "Please tella you mother-in-law, if she wanna come back, she come. But she no come, January first I'ma gonna let the apartment go. I no gonna pay for thisa big apartment ifa she gonna keep a leave."

Although it was uncomfortable to be placed in the middle of their marital difficulties, I relayed the message to Mom Serino. Her response was a stubborn, "If he wants me to come back, he has to come out here and ask me himself."

"Mom," I said, "you know he isn't going to do that."

"Well, if he wants me to come back, that's what he has to do." The line had been drawn in the sand. There were now five days remaining for the standoff to end.

I felt sorry for my mother-in-law. While she was a very difficult person to live with, the idea of living in an apartment with a philandering husband was certainly not ideal. Yet what were her options? Dolores had tolerated the vacillation long enough and refused to enable her mother in her ambivalence any longer. Unfortunately, it was extremely short notice to find an apartment for her. I spoke to Tom about the situation. "What if she came and stayed with us for a little while, Tommy, just until she and your father straighten this problem out?"

"Doris, this problem is older than you are," he responded. "It's never going to be resolved."

"Well, we can't put her out on the street. What's she going to do?"

"She'll have to go back to the apartment. I agree with Dolores this time. Ma can't keep playing these games."

"But you know how stubborn she is. She's not going to go back since Pop gave her that ultimatum. And you know that Pop is not going to come out here and beg her to come back."

"Look, Doris. I want you to understand that if we take her in here, you won't get any thanks for it. She won't treat you well and she'll be completely unappreciative."

"She's your mother, Tom. I don't see that we really have any choice. Let's just hope that she goes back to the apartment before the first of the year."

I spoke to Mom Serino the next day. "Mom, why don't you go back to the apartment? You know that's where you want to be."

"I'm not going back until he comes out here and asks me himself," she insisted.

"Mom, you know that he's never going to do that. Then what will you do?" I reasoned.

Mom was obstinate in her position, and at the predetermined time, Pop relinquished their large apartment on Church Street and moved into a two-room attic apartment on Academy Street by himself. Mom was furious. She screamed and cried and pouted for days. Tom and Jerry went to the apartment to retrieve her belongings, and she began her journey with us.

Mom Serino spent over a year with us. It was the most challenging year of our married lives. I understand that she was unhappy. She didn't want to live with us. She wanted to live with her husband. She wanted things to be different between them, and she also realized they would never be.

We had three bedrooms in our house: one for Tom and me, one for the boys, and now one for Mom Serino. We had no bed for her, so she brought a roll-up cot from her apartment. It took several weeks to organize her belongings, so until her motivation increased, her room was a chaotic mess of boxes, clothes, and random items, leaving no room for her bed.

Therefore, every night when she wanted to go to bed, she would roll the cot out of her cluttered room and into the living room, set the bed up, crawl between the sheets, and go to sleep. It didn't matter whether Tom and I were watching TV or playing a game at the dining room table on the opposite side of the room, or even if we had company. She was completely self-absorbed. After several weeks with no progress on her bedroom, I took the initiative to organize the room.

"Mom, I'm going to help you put your room in order today," I said one morning after Tom had left for work.

"No, I'll get to it," she replied.

"It's already been several weeks and you haven't started, so I'm going to help you today. Let me clean the kitchen and get Joey's bottles ready, then we can attack those boxes." By the time I had completed my maternal and scullery duties and entered her room to assist with the cleanup, Mom had already begun and the project was well underway. By the day after next, she was sleeping in her room.

Living with Tom's mother was very difficult. There were times when she could be good company and people enjoyed being with her. She was a good sport and was often the brunt of jokes. On Saint Patrick's Day, Tom and our neighbor Bob dyed her white hair green while she slept on a lawn chair. When she awoke, she feigned anger and chased them all around the yard with a dishtowel. She went on vacation with my parents several times. They took her to Orchard Beach, Howe Caverns, Ausable Chasm, and every place they went, she was pleasant and sociable. Yet if she was upset or something didn't go the way she wanted, she would lock herself in her room and pout. She wouldn't speak to anyone, and this mood could last for hours or days.

I was a young wife with two little ones, both with special needs, and by May I was pregnant with our third child. She could have been a great help but rather chose to live separate from us while under the same roof.

One summer day when I was about four months pregnant, Tessie came over to find me on my knees, scrubbing the kitchen floor. Mom was in a lounge chair in the back yard. "What are you doing, Doris?" Tessie asked.

"I'm scrubbing the floor," I responded rhetorically.

"She's out there sunning herself, and you're four months pregnant and scrubbing the floor!"

I stopped, looked up at her, and said, "What can you do?" Mom could have been a tremendous help to us, but she never felt obliged to assist in any way.

One day in early autumn, Mom "took a spell." I don't know what triggered her emotional outburst or the subsequent extreme behavior. It happened abruptly, without warning or prompting. After dinner while Tom and I were sitting out on the lawn with Bob and Tessie, Mom started screaming, burst through the front door, and began running down the dirt road to the school parking lot.

Tom and Bob ran after her and took her back to the house and got her settled in her room, while I called the doctor. Within fifteen minutes the doctor arrived, and he examined her while we waited in the living room. Finally, he came out and spoke to us. "Could you give me a little more time with her, please? If you all would just step outside for a moment, I'd like to have a talk with her."

We walked over to Bob and Tessie's house and were standing in the lot when the doctor could be heard reproving Mom sharply. "There is nothing at all wrong with you, Mrs. Serino! You just want attention, and this is no way to get it! You are as healthy as I am. You're simply bored and need something to do. I suggest that you get a job. You are well enough to work. Go and get a job and be productive. Find something to do!" We were shocked at how angry he was. He called her selfish and histrionic, and reproved her for unnecessary drama and upsetting two households for no good purpose.

When he came out of the house, he calmly told us that she should find a job because she had too much time on her hands. She never got a job. Financially she didn't need to since Pop Serino sent her money every week, and truthfully if she was bored, there was plenty to do around the house.

All these antics created tension and friction in our home, and Tom and I were frequently at odds because of her actions. Nevertheless, all these things paled in comparison to the hostility she was creating between our children by her favoritism. As a mother she had favored Jerry to the exclusion of Tom. Now she was doing the same with my boys. Each morning she would come out of her room and find the boys playing in the living room. She would go over to Joey, pick him up, and hug and kiss him while Tommy just watched.

"Mom!" I would say and then glance over at Tommy.

"Oh. Good morning, Tommy," she would say and continue to ignore him while lavishing affection on Joey. Finally, she'd look at Tommy. "Well, are you going to kiss me or not?"

Tommy would fold his arms. "No. I don't like you."

Soon Tommy started doing small vindictive acts toward her, and they escalated in their scope. On one occasion, Tommy snuck into her room, found an afghan she was almost finished crocheting, and unraveled the entire thing, leaving it a tangled mess of yarn.

That night I had a serious talk with Tom. "I'm very concerned about the effect your mother is having on the boys," I began. "You know she favors Joey, and Tommy has been doing spiteful things to her."

"What kind of things?" Tom asked.

"I told you before how he colored on her suitcase and how he took her perfume and dumped it down the toilet. Well, today he unraveled the entire blanket she's been crocheting. Look, I know that these are not major catastrophes, but they're vindictive actions by a little boy who feels

TOM SERINO

hurt." I shook my head. "Tom, I see how she treats him and how he looks at her with pent-up anger. I can't have her doing to our children what she did to her own children."

"So, what do you want me to do?" my frustrated husband responded.

"Nothing. I'm going to call your sister, and together she and I are going to find an apartment for your mother."

I was now almost to term in my pregnancy, and because Joey had been a cesarean birth, our next child would be delivered the same way. So, after Christmas we scheduled the surgery for the second week of January, according to the date estimated by Dr. Perino.

Just before my third son was born, Mom Serino went to visit relatives in Pittsfield, Massachusetts. She often would go and visit friends or relatives and stay for a week or two, then return, although she never would say that she was going or when she was coming back. She would just go. Now, just before I went into the hospital to have my third child, she left and didn't return for six weeks.

When I came home from the hospital with Robert, my mother came and stayed with me for a week. I really needed the help since I had a C-section incision, an infant, and two toddlers, one in a Frejka brace. As always my parents were prepared to lend aid. My mother cared for me and my boys with the tenderness and capability of an angel of mercy. My father would come out every night and have supper with us, then go back home. I don't know what I would have done without my mother during that time.

When I had recovered enough, I called Dolores. "We have to talk about your mother," I said after we'd exchanged greetings. "I really can't take much more of it. She's putting a wedge between me and your brother and

THROUGH MY MOTHER'S EYES

causing tension with my children. She can't stay here any longer."

"Well, she can't come here," Delores told me.

"I'm not asking you to take her, Dolores. I'm asking you to help me find an apartment for her. She's away now, and I don't know when she'll be back, but I'd like to have a place for her to go when she returns."

Dolores didn't argue. "Okay, Doris. I'll pick you up tomorrow and we'll go find a place for her."

"Fine," I said. "I'm going to call Pop and let him know what's going on."

It took several days and we saw many places, but Dolores and I finally found an apartment at 210 Main Street, right in the heart of Poughkeepsie. It was a nice apartment, spacious and bright, and a short walk from the local merchants. We knew it was perfect for her.

Mom had lived in the building on Main Street for about a year when Pop Serino heard that the city was converting the old King's Court Hotel into apartments, and he talked to some people in charge and was able to get her an apartment there. The building had a beautiful lobby where all the women would sit and talk. So, after one year she moved from Lower Main Street to King's Court. Pop continued to pay for the apartment and the utilities and gave Mom money each week. She lived there for the rest of her life.

When she came home from Massachusetts, I approached her. "Mom, Dolores and I have found an apartment for you. You'll have your own place. It's on Lower Main Street and within walking distance of all the shops you like." She seemed unfazed by the news, so I continued. "It's a nice, large apartment and Pop has already covered the cost. You can move in immediately."

It took several days to pack her belongings and transport them to the new apartment. The day she left, we went to her bedroom to ensure she hadn't forgotten anything. Mom turned to me, and without warning she embraced me. "I'm sorry for all the trouble I caused you," she said.

I wanted to respond with warmth, but ambivalence arose in its place. She had been the cause of much difficulty for us over the past year, yet I held no animosity toward her. She was an unhappy woman, but in her sadness and pain, she hurt those around her. While I regretted that her time with us was unpleasant, I was relieved that she would no longer be directly involved in our daily lives.

As I held her, I encompassed her brokenness and for a brief moment surrounded her with acceptance. "Let's go, Mom. Tom is waiting in the car."

As the car drove away to open a new chapter in Mom's life, I breathed a silent prayer for her wounded heart—and mine.

TWENTY-FIVE

The Remaining Years

I was startled awake by the high-pitched whirring of a circular saw that seemed to emanate from my kitchen. It was a beautiful morning, and the warm prevernal breeze carried the songs of returning robins and the agitated caws of the blue jays through my window. Usually this was a most pleasant way to awaken on a Saturday in April, but today was different. Tom had begun construction on the staircase from the kitchen to the basement so I would no longer need to carry laundry outside and into the cellar—if the Bilco doors weren't frozen shut, anyway. The minor inconvenience of noise and dust was gratefully endured for the sake of easy passage to my laundry area.

The staircase was the first of countless alterations made to our home, as the years passed, to accommodate the contemporary needs of our growing family. I painted the walls throughout the house after the plaster had cured. Finally, after one year of dull white walls, I had a rainbow of colors from room to room. My living room furniture was beige, so I painted the walls pink and covered one wall with burgundy wallpaper and complimented the ensemble with a beige rug in the center of the hardwood floors. Over the years I changed the colors many times; my walls were painted every color imaginable. Tom made cornices for the windows in the living room, which was the style of the day in the early 1960s. Cornices could be made from wood or various types of materials, and the wooden cornices Tom made lasted several decades.

Our lawn came in full and lush in the summer. Bob's mother, Mrs. O, lived in the farmhouse on Vassar Road, and she had several large lilac bushes and offered Tom some cuttings for planting. We ended up with ten lilac trees, white and lavender colored, lining the border between our property and the lot. They yielded thousands of flowers over the decades.

Tom's Aunt Tessie and Uncle Mike came out several times a week to visit. Uncle Mike loved working in the yard, and Tom allowed him liberty to plant anything he wanted. He planted two rose of Sharon bushes, shrubbery along the side of the driveway, several yews, and a large vegetable garden in the back yard. Uncle Mike wasn't always cautious with the placement of his pastoral creations, though. He once planted a row of crocuses across the middle of the front yard, running diagonal rather than parallel to the house.

The last thing planted by Uncle Mike before he passed was a small maple tree near the lilac bushes. Our children would jump over the tree, and Uncle Mike was afraid they would break it, so he placed stakes around it to prevent any injury to the tree. Uncle Mike passed away in 1967, but today the maple tree still stands—over fifty feet tall. That year I had my fifth child, a boy who I named Michael. Aunt Tessie became his godmother.

Over the years, Tom and I were constantly changing the house—I on the inside and he outside. I would arrange furniture, paint walls, exchange rooms, tear out closets, and whatever else I thought would make better sense for a growing family. Tom once said, "When I come home at night, I'm never sure in which room I'm sleeping!"

"It's not a boring life with me," I retorted. I truly made life interesting for him.

When our children started school, it created a small problem for the school district. There was no place for a bus to safely pick up the children. Since we lived next door to the school, it was decided that my children would be walkers. I instructed them to walk along the grass after the buses had discharged their passengers and departed, then stood on the front patio and watched them as they ran, sauntered, and otherwise trudged their way to school.

In the wintertime when snow made walking on the grass impossible, I would often accompany them across the parking lot. Joey was still on crutches when he started school, yet he made the journey to school just as the other children, although the winter created a unique problem for him. He had great difficulty maneuvering the crutches over the icy blacktop and snowbanks, so the school staff intervened. Mrs. McNamara, the school nurse, and Mrs. Nawroki, the school secretary, met Joey and me at the snowbanks along the edge of the school property, then carried him across the parking lot to the school. Over the six decades we lived in this house, Vassar Road School has proven to be a most considerate neighbor.

After our daughter Annmarie was born in 1964, Tom decided that we needed a garage. So, in the spring of 1965, we began construction on a two-car garage. I'm not mistaken in saying "we" built the garage, for despite having four little children, I worked side by side with Tom in the construction. He laid the block and I assisted with the woodwork. At the age of thirty-two, with three little boys and an infant girl observing from the front lawn, I helped Tom set the ridge board for the roof.

"Tom, I don't think this is a good idea," I told him. "Why don't you wait until Ray can come over and help?"

"No, Doris, I don't have time for that. I'm going to hand the ridge board up to you and you place it on the joist. Then I'm going up the ladder with the other end of the ridge board. You just hold the board so it doesn't fall back down to the ground, okay?"

So Tom hoisted the heavy piece of lumber up to me and I placed it on the joist.

"Okay, now I'm going to walk the other end over to the ladder. Make sure it doesn't fall." Tom began to walk up the ladder, and I saw the ridge board shift precariously close to the edge of the joist. Tom adjusted the ridge board so it wouldn't shift when we lifted it, then dragged the ladder to my side and ascended the ladder. "Okay, good. Now we have to lift the ridge board and I'll nail it in place. I'm going to place this two-by-four under the ridge board to support most of the weight. Do you think you can hold it steady while I nail it?"

"Tom, I've had four children. I can do anything."

He smiled. "I know you can. All right, now on three I'm going to lift it and you press it firmly against the rafter." Giving a small grunt, Tom lifted the ridge board and put the two-by-four in place. "Okay, Doris, hold it tight."

As he placed the first nail, the ridge board shifted slightly. "I told you to hold it, Doris!"

"Don't you yell at me, Tommy Serino, or I'll knock you off this roof!" I yelled back.

He adjusted the ridge board and quickly nailed it in place as I pressed against it with all my strength. The next few nails were simple. Once the ridge board was set, the rafters went up quickly, as I had found my sea legs and moved without fear like a master roofer.

Our house became a focal point in our family for decades. Kay and Ray bought a house less than a mile down the road from us, and every Saturday night they would visit with their family. We would have coffee and something sweet while the children played outside or in the basement, which had become a finished playroom.

On Sunday mornings, we would attend church on Union Street at the Church of the Nativity until it was demolished in the mid-sixties. Then after church we would walk up the street to Aunt Tessie and Uncle Mike's apartment, where it seemed that the entire city of Poughkeepsie had assembled. Aunt Tessie's kitchen was large and became the place where visitors gathered.

Everyone sat at the king-sized kitchen table, which hosted between ten and twenty people, depending on the week. They had a table positioned by the entry door covered with breakfast pastry, coffee cakes, and rolls, and there were two pots of coffee available: a white percolator with tiny blue flowers at the center of the pot filled with brown coffee, and a macchinetta filled with black coffee. Tom always sent me ahead with the children while he stopped at Honey's Bakery to get crumb buns.

When he came in, Uncle Mike would exclaim loudly, "Looka! Tommy, he comea now. He no helpa Doris. She gotta lotta kids, e he no helpa." Then he would laugh.

Aunt Tessie would reprove Tom for buying more buns when there was already plenty to go around. "You take these home, Tommy. They'll be your breakfast tomorrow."

Then she would kiss his cheek. She genuinely loved her nephew.

We would visit for a few hours, then it was home for dinner. After dinner we would get together with Kay, Ray, and the children. We alternated, one week at her house, the next week at our house. When the Sunday gathering was at our home, we often had family games outside in the schoolyard. We played kickball and softball together, and in the winter the dads and kids would sled down the inclined front yard while the moms prepared hot chocolate for half-frozen children.

Sundays saw other visitors join our family group. In addition to Mom and Pop Messina, who were always present, Aunt Eleanor and Uncle Carm, Aunt Betty and Uncle Okey, and many others were frequently in attendance.

In the early seventies, Kay, Ray, Tom, and I became friends with Dick and Emmie Sara, the owners of a local small Italian restaurant, and we began patronizing their bistro every Friday night. Tommy was now old enough to watch the other children, so we joined the singalong hosted by Dick Sara. When Tommy left for college, Joe watched the other children, who were then old enough to require little oversight. We would stay out until Dick closed the place and a group of us would go out for breakfast. We were often out until four in the morning and continued this tradition for many years.

Time passes more rapidly than we can perceive, and soon the neighborhood began to change. Andy Leto died suddenly in the seventies. Earl Bruno in the mid-nineties and Bob Ostrander, our closest neighbor, in 1997. As the last man from our generation, Tom took the responsibility to look after their widows, Tessie, Madge, and Rita. He would visit them, do small chores or repairs as needed, and just talk with friends who now faced the world alone.

When the last of the women passed away, Tom took his place as watchman over the community he had helped to build. He sat on the front porch and waved to the children in the school buses as they entered the parking lot. Soon the parents, teachers, and bus drivers would all greet him as the ambassador of goodwill he had become. Often the teachers would park their cars and walk up to Tom on the porch and chat with him. The school maintenance workers frequently visited to sit and talk. When the time came that Tom could no longer walk, the maintenance men would shovel the snow from our driveway. Tom, who always cared deeply for everyone, was now receiving the rewards of his benevolence.

We lived together in this house that Tom built with his own hands for sixty-two years. We raised five children and were gifted with fourteen grandchildren and thirteen great-grandchildren. We hosted holidays, birthdays, anniversaries, graduations, wedding receptions, Sunday get-togethers, Cub Scout meetings, Little League and CYO picnics, and a myriad of other events. This house has seen lots of life and even more living.

On the night Tom died, he wouldn't allow me to call the ambulance. He knew he was dying and wanted to leave this world from his own home. Sometimes the house is lonely now, but it's never empty. It is filled with people, filled with memories, filled with love, and filled with the presence of a man who learned to love unreservedly because he was loved unconditionally by an innocent young woman he met at a candy store on Union Street.

Epilogue

My mother is now silent. Her eyes are tired and moist. Her face is drawn, and she appears exhausted after a long journey through her reminiscences.

"Ma," I say, touching her hand. "Ma, are you feeling all right?"

She looks up at me, moving her head as if with a great effort, and stares.

"Ma, are you okay?"

Gathering her strength, she blinks. "Yes, honey. Yes, I'm fine. I'm just a little tired, that's all." As she moves to stand, she realizes that she still has the photo of her and Dad in her hand. She looks at the picture that has prompted so many thoughts and memories, then touches it gently, caressing the glass on the faded portrait. Finally, she tenderly places it on the tray table next to her chair.

Again, she starts to rise from the chair, and I reach out to assist her gallant effort, pausing to ensure her balance before embracing her gently.

"I think I'll go to bed now," is all she says.

"Okay, Ma. Good night. I'll see you in the morning. I love you."

When she's only two steps away from me, she stops and turns to smile at me. "I love you, too, baby."

Later, as she lay in bed, she felt the chill of the night air creeping under the blanket and quilt, stirring her into a state of semi-consciousness. Her dreams both concern and excite her. She's thinking of Tom, and when her thoughts become dreams is uncertain. They blend as one.

She finds herself walking on Union Street in the direction of Perry Street. Her dream is vivid, life-like with a crispness she has not before known. She can feel the uneven hardness of the concrete beneath her feet. She sees the brick road and the houses she remembers in pristine condition. She hears the chimes on the Church of the Nativity strike three and suddenly hears Tommy's voice call, "Doris!" As she's wondering if her imagination is taking advantage of her, she hears it a second time. "Doris!"

There's no mistaking the voice. It's Tommy. She walks toward the sound of his voice, though she doesn't understand how she's walking so effortlessly.

A young man stands on the corner of Union and Perry Streets. His face is so clear, so lively, and she's certain she recognizes him.

"Hello, Doris," he says as she nears him.

There in front of the candy store stands Tommy— young and wholesome, his welcoming smile greeting her with anticipation. She quickens her pace with ease, moving painlessly toward him. She embraces him and feels his strong arms surround her.

It's not a dream after all.

About the Author

Tom Serino was born and raised in Poughkeepsie, New York, and presently lives in Telford, Pennsylvania, with his wife, Donna. Together they have three children and four grandchildren and have also cared for thirty foster children. He is a graduate of SUNY Oswego, Valley Forge Christian College, and Biblical Theological Seminary.

Made in United States
North Haven, CT
20 December 2024

63156275R00164